Healthy Living with

high
CHOLESTEROL

Published in 2011 by Murdoch Books Pty Limited
www.murdochbooks.com.au

Murdoch Books Australia
Pier 8/9
23 Hickson Road
Millers Point NSW 2000
Phone: +61 (0) 2 8220 2000
Fax: +61 (0) 2 8220 2558

Murdoch Books UK Limited
Erico House
6th Floor North
93–99 Upper Richmond Road
Putney, London SW15 2TG
Phone: +44 (0) 20 8785 5995
Fax: +44 (0) 20 8785 5985

For Corporate Orders & Custom Publishing contact
Noel Hammond, National Business Development Manager

Publisher: Lynn Lewis
Designer: Lena Lowe
Recipe consultant and nutrition analyst: Susanna Holt
Food Consultant: Jayne Tancred
Photographers: Jared Fowler and Ian Hofstetter
Stylists: Jane Collins, Katy Holder and Cherise Koch
Food preparation: Joanne Kelly and Alan Wilson
Recipes by: Michelle Earl and members of the Murdoch Books Test Kitchen
Project Editor: Alice Grundy
Production: Joan Beal

National Library of Australia Cataloguing-in-Publication Data
ISBN: 978-1-74266-410-1 (pbk.)
Series: Healthy eating.
Notes: Includes index.
Subjects: Low-cholesterol diet--Recipes.
             Cooking.
Dewey Number: 641.563847

A catalogue record for this book is available from the British Library.

Printed by 1010 Printing International Limited. PRINTED IN CHINA.

IMPORTANT: Those who might be at risk from the effects of salmonella poisoning (the elderly, pregnant women, young children and those suffering from immune deficiency diseases) should consult their doctor with any concerns about eating raw eggs.

OVEN GUIDE: You may find cooking times vary depending on the oven you are using. For fan-forced ovens, as a general rule, set the oven temperature to 20°C (35°F) lower than indicated in the recipe.

Healthy Living with
high
CHOLESTEROL

EASY *low-cholesterol*
RECIPES AND LIFESTYLE SOLUTIONS

Introductory text by Karen Kingham (nutritionist)

MURDOCH BOOKS

contents

Living with high cholesterol   **6**

Breakfast   **26**

Snacks, light meals and sides   **46**

Soups and salads   **62**

Main meals   **84**

Vegetarian meals   **128**

Sweet things   **164**

Index   **186**

Contact information   **192**

Lower
cholesterol
THE HEALTHY WAY

High blood cholesterol is one of the major risk factors for heart disease, which can lead to heart attack or stroke. Simply put, the higher your cholesterol level, the greater your risk. Cardiovascular disease (CVD) is the leading cause of death in the world, and is expected to become an even greater health problem over the next 20 years.

The good news is that the lower your cholesterol, the lower your risk of CVD and the less chance you have of becoming a health statistic.

There is plenty you can do to lower your cholesterol, the most important of which is improving your diet and lifestyle. Cholesterol-reducing diets can be both flavoursome and colourful, and the recipes in this book are ideal to enjoy with family and friends. Lower your cholesterol and you just might live a longer, healthier life.

Cholesterol is a waxy, fatty substance that's made by the liver. It also enters your body in some of the foods you eat.

What is cholesterol?

Cholesterol is a waxy, fatty substance that's made by the liver. It also enters your body in some of the foods you eat, such as shellfish, meat, chicken, eggs, butter, cheese and whole milk.

Because cholesterol is a fat and can't dissolve in the blood, it needs to be carried to and from the cells via transporters or carriers called lipoproteins. There are two types of lipoproteins you should be aware of:

Low-density lipoprotein or LDL cholesterol: This is found in the greatest amounts and is the one you most need to worry about, so it's sometimes referred to as 'bad' cholesterol.

LDL's main job is to take cholesterol from the liver to the body cells where it's needed. Too much LDL causes a build-up of cholesterol on the inside of blood vessel walls, which is not good for your health.

High-density lipoprotein or HDL cholesterol: This is the cholesterol you want to have more of, and is sometimes referred to as 'good' cholesterol. HDL tidies up excess cholesterol, picking it up from your blood vessels and enabling it to be broken down by the liver or transported out of your body as waste.

The trouble with too much LDL cholesterol

Too much LDL cholesterol in your blood causes the excess to be deposited in the blood vessels. Over time, the cholesterol (along with other substances) builds up around the vessel walls causing them to narrow and then harden—think of the sludge you might get clogging up your drainpipes at home. This process is known as atherosclerosis.

Cholesterol isn't bad for you in the right quantities. You actually need it for your body's hormone production, coating your nerve cells and forming cell membranes. However, an excess of foods containing saturated and trans fats can upset the body's cholesterol balance by causing your liver to make more cholesterol than it otherwise would.

Cholesterol deposited in the blood vessels is also more susceptible to a process known as oxidation. When LDL is oxidised it becomes more irritating to the blood vessels, causes inflammation, and accelerates the process of atherosclerosis.

Atherosclerosis is involved in the progression of a number of diseases:

- Coronary heart disease occurs when the blood vessels to the heart are affected by atherosclerosis; it may lead to angina or heart attack.
- Cerebrovascular disease is caused by narrowing or blockages in blood vessels to the brain and may result in a stroke.
- Peripheral vascular disease (also known as peripheral arterial disease) is the result of narrowing or blockage of the blood vessels in parts of the body other than the brain or heart, most commonly the arteries supplying the legs and feet.

Along with a few other (less common) diseases of the heart and blood vessels, these conditions caused by atherosclerosis are collectively known as CVD, the number one cause of death in the world.

Your cholesterol target

Regardless of how high your total blood cholesterol is, the lower your LDL cholesterol the better off you'll be.

Your doctor will determine your target cholesterol levels after taking into account a wide range of factors that determine your personal risk of developing CVD, including your family history, whether you're a smoker, and your body weight.

For example, if you're not already at increased risk of cardiovascular disease, it's likely you'll be advised to keep your total cholesterol below 5.0 mmol/L and your LDL level below 3.0 mmol/L. Those with a high degree of risk may be told to aim for less than 2 mmol/L of LDL, accompanied by HDL levels of more than 1.0 mmol/L. Note that aside from your personal health and lifestyle factors, these targets may vary depending upon where in the world you live.

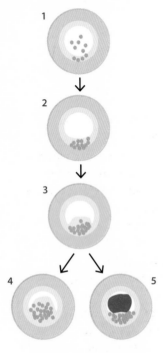

1   cholesterol particles travel
     through blood vessels

2–3 cholesterol builds up on
     blood vessel walls

4   almost complete blockage

5   blood clots may block
     completely

What's between you and your target

A number of factors can cause your cholesterol to rise. Some of them you can change, some you can't.

Factors you can't change include:

○ **Your age and gender:** blood cholesterol tends to rise as we get older and is usually higher in men than women until after menopause. A woman's cholesterol may quickly catch up to that of men of a similar age once menopause is over.

○ **Your inheritance:** high blood cholesterol can run in families and your genes may also put you at greater risk.

Below are some of the factors you can change. Behaviour-related risk factors like these are responsible for around 80 per cent of coronary heart disease and cerebrovascular disease.

○ **Your weight:** as your weight increases so too does the likelihood that your LDL cholesterol will be higher and HDL lower than is ideal.

○ **Your diet:** eating a diet high in saturated fat is one of the most significant causes of high LDL cholesterol. Major sources of saturated fat in the diet include butter, cream, cheese and other full-fat dairy products; fat from meat and poultry (including processed meats such as sausages and salami). Significant amounts of saturated fat are also found in many baked goods such as biscuits (cookies), cakes, pies, pastries; fried take-away foods and snack foods like chocolate, potato chips (crisps), corn chips and cheese-flavoured snacks.

○ **How much you move:** being physically active helps lower your LDL cholesterol and reduces your risk of CVD by lowering blood pressure, insulin resistance and body weight. Being more physically active also helps keep your bones and joints healthy, and lowers your risk of developing type 2 diabetes, obesity, depression and some types of cancer.

LDL cholesterol build-up

As LDL cholesterol builds up in the blood it becomes deposited on the inner wall of the blood vessel. Over time the blood vessel becomes narrow and clogged, making it harder for blood to pass through. The blood vessel may eventually become completely blocked or the narrowed vessel can more easily become blocked by a blood clot or other debris.

If you have high blood cholesterol, have you considered how high your risk of CVD is and what your chances are of having a heart attack or suffering from a stroke?

What about triglycerides?

If you've had a cholesterol test, the results probably included information about triglycerides: these fats are found in food and are also made by the body. Any kilojoules you consume but don't use immediately for energy are converted to triglycerides and then stored in fat cells. This especially applies to excess kilojoules consumed in the form of carbohydrates such as sugars, soft drinks (soda) or alcohol.

The link between high triglycerides and CVD remains unclear, but when blood triglyceride levels are high, your risk of heart problems is usually high too.

Triglyceride levels tend to be high if you drink alcohol to excess, are obese, don't exercise enough or if you eat too many refined carbohydrates. Type 2 diabetes and some other diseases can also increase your chances of having high triglycerides, as can genetic factors.

Aim to keep your triglycerides below 1.5 mmol/L by following the advice given in this book, increasing your activity levels, drinking less alcohol and reducing your intake of fats. Swap refined or high glycaemic index (GI) carbohydrates (which are converted into energy quickly and can negatively impact your blood sugar) for slow-burning wholegrain and low-GI options too.

Risk factors for cardiovascular disease

If you have high blood cholesterol, have you considered how high your risk of CVD is and what your chances are of having a heart attack or stroke? These are important questions that everyone with high cholesterol should know the answers to.

In general, the higher your LDL cholesterol level and the more risk factors you have, the greater your chances of developing CVD and having a heart attack or stroke. Fortunately, by living a

Your risk in percentage terms is best calculated by your doctor, however you can get a rough idea by considering how many of these risk factors apply to you:

- High total and/or LDL cholesterol
- Low HDL cholesterol
- High triglycerides
- Cigarette smoking
- High blood pressure (for example, over 140/90 mmHg)
- Overweight and obesity
- Inactivity
- Diabetes or pre-diabetes
- Stress, depression and social isolation
- Aged over 45 years
- Family history of heart disease (i.e. a parent or sibling affected before 60 years of age)
- Kidney transplant or kidney disease
- Aboriginal, Torres Strait Islander, Maori or Pacific Islander descent
- Asian or from the Indian subcontinent
- African or Mexican American

healthier life you can make a real difference to many of your risk factors. In short, give up smoking, take charge of your diet and get out of the house and move more.

Women take care

Cardiovascular disease claims the lives of many thousands of women every year, yet high blood cholesterol and CVD are often dismissed by women as being male problems. Blood cholesterol levels can rise significantly after menopause, but prior to that protective female hormones give women an extra 10 to 15 years of good cardiovascular health compared with men. With these extra years you have a valuable opportunity to take care of yourself and minimise the cardiovascular consequences of menopause.

The issue of weight

Carrying too much weight increases your risk of high cholesterol and CVD as well as many other health problems. Being overweight is defined as having a body mass index (BMI) of 25 or more. If you know your weight and height, you can work out your BMI by dividing your weight in kilograms into your height in metres, squared. For example, if you weigh 75 kilograms and are 150 cm (1.5 metres) tall, your BMI is 75 divided by 2.25 (i.e. 1.5 x 1.5) = 33.3.

In general your BMI is a good indicator of your body fat levels and health risks. But there are some groups of people—such as athletes and those of some ethnic groups (for example, Pacific Islanders and South-East Asians) to whom this rule does not apply.

Fat stored around your tummy (giving you an apple shape) puts you at greater risk than fat stored on your hips and thighs (giving you a pear shape).

Having a large waist size makes you a bigger candidate for a heart attack or stroke. You can check yours using a tape measure at the level of your belly button. Caucasian and Asian women should aim for a waist less than 80 cm (31½ in) and Caucasian men less than 94 cm (37 in).

Optimum waist measurements are yet to be determined for some ethnic groups; it is considered likely that Asian men may need to aim for a slightly lower waist measurement than Caucasian men, and a slightly higher measurement may be applicable to African Americans and Pacific Islanders of both sexes.

Changes for a lower cholesterol diet

Healthier eating habits

Adopting better eating and lifestyle habits is the most important step you can take to lower your blood cholesterol. That's why your doctor will usually give you a chance to try these steps before prescribing you any medication. These changes are also the best way to prevent high cholesterol in the first place.

The benefits of the lowering your LDL cholesterol and increasing your HDL levels are well proven, and there's no better motivator for sticking to your new healthier habits than seeing the improvements in your test results for yourself, so ask your doctor how often you should get your cholesterol re-tested.

For the health of your heart and blood vessels, you need to get back to basics and embrace natural, unprocessed foods such as:

○ wholegrains, legumes and fresh fruit and vegetables for their antioxidants, phytochemicals (plant chemicals) and low-GI carbohydrates
○ nuts, seeds and more fish for their healthier fats
○ lean meat, chicken, seafood and low fat dairy products for vital protein.

Many foods have proven heart health benefits, and some of them will be discussed in the following pages. But no single food will keep cholesterol at bay. Success is only possible by including as many heart-friendly foods in your diet as possible. Healthy eating habits add up, and if you follow all the advice given here your blood cholesterol may drop by as much as a 15 per cent.

Don't despair if you don't manage to follow all the advice given here. Start with the most important—cutting down on saturated fat. Use our guides and tips to identify saturated fats and remove them from your diet. Once you've successfully implemented this change start on another, then another, until you've made them all. If you're finding it hard to achieve our advice or if you have diabetes, kidney disease or any other serious medical problems, seek the advice of a dietitian.

Research now shows that while it's important to keep your dietary intake of cholesterol down, it's not necessary to avoid it entirely, since cholesterol from food has relatively little impact on your blood cholesterol levels, especially when your diet is generally healthy. Many cholesterol-containing foods like eggs, prawns and other crustaceans are also low in saturated fat and can be good sources of heart-friendly omega-3 fats.

Where's the cholesterol?

Food	Cholesterol mg (approx)
Liver (beef), 100 g	380
Egg, 1 large	216
Prawns, 100 g	250
Lobster, 100 g	145
Beef sirloin (trimmed of fat), 100 g	90

Limit your cholesterol intake

Moderation in dietary cholesterol does, however, remain the key. Expert opinion varies, but limiting your intake of eggs to six a week and having the occasional meal of prawns cooked without added fat is unlikely to do most people with high cholesterol any harm. If you have familial hypercholesterolaemia or a very high risk of heart disease you may be an exception to this advice and should be stricter with your cholesterol intake.

Health authorities recommend that people with healthy cholesterol levels keep their dietary cholesterol intake below 300 mg per day, while those who have high cholesterol or are taking cholesterol-lowering medicines should aim for less than 200 mg per day.

Cut the bad fat

Just as there are good and bad types of blood cholesterol, there are good and bad fats. Rather than banishing all fat from your diet, the best thing you can do to get your cholesterol down is to achieve the right balance of healthy and unhealthy fats.

Saturated fats and trans fats are the biggest culprits when it comes to raising your LDL cholesterol level.

Saturated fats are usually of animal origin (except for palm oil and coconut fat). Trans fats occur naturally in some foods of animal origin such as beef, lamb and dairy foods. They are also created when liquid vegetable oils are turned into hard fats (margarines and solid frying fats) for commercial food production. This process is known as hydrogenation or partial hydrogenation.

Maintaining a healthy weight

Here are some of the reasons you should aim to keep your weight down using a heart-healthy diet and regular exercise:

Heart health benefits

- Lower LDL cholesterol
- Higher HDL cholesterol
- Lower triglycerides
- Lower blood pressure
- Improve insulin resistance and control blood glucose if you have diabetes
- Reduce your risk of CVD

General health benefits

- Reduce risk of type 2 diabetes
- Lower risk of some cancers
- Improve sleep apnoea
- Reduce joint pain in arthritis
- Control gout
- Lower risk of gall bladder disease
- Improve asthma
- Relieve reflux
- Improve fertility

Where is the bad fat?

Ridding your diet of saturated and trans fats takes practice. Consider the following tips for ousting these bad guys from your life:

- Avoid butter, lard, cream, sour cream, coconut milk or cream and hard cooking margarines
- Choose lean cuts of meat and trim any remaining fat before cooking
- Choose skinless cuts of chicken or remove the skin before eating
- Eat cheese less often and choose lower fat varieties
- Avoid processed meats like hot dogs, bacon, devon, chicken loaf and salami
- Use low- or reduced-fat milk, yoghurt, ice cream and custard
- Avoid deep-fried takeaway foods, pies, sausage rolls and pasties
- Choose tomato-based pasta sauces over creamy types
- Save commercial biscuits (cookies), cakes, muffins, pastries and puddings for special occasions
- Cut back on high-fat snack foods, such as chocolate bars, potato chips (crisps) and savoury crackers
- Cook with low fat methods: steaming, grilling, dry frying, baking and barbecuing

Major sources of trans fats include crackers, biscuits (cookies), doughnuts, corn and potato chips (crisps), margarine, hot chips and other commercially produced fried foods—anything prepared using hydrogenated or partially hydrogenated oils. Some countries have higher levels of trans fats in their foods than others, but this is changing as governments become more aware of the health threat they pose and place pressure on food industries to lower the amount of trans fats in the foods they produce. Cutting back on saturated and trans fats and using healthier monounsaturated and polyunsaturated fats will help lower LDL and raise HDL cholesterol. Our easy-to-read table below helps you find these bad fats so you can make better choices when you shop.

Include a good balance of polyunsaturated and monounsaturated fats in your diet by thinking about variety. Try sunflower or canola oil for baking, macadamia, walnut or extra virgin olive oil for salad dressings, and peanut or sesame oil for Asian stir-fries. Similarly, replace the butter on your bread with avocado, low-fat dips, peanut butter, low-fat ricotta or cottage

What fat is that?

Fat	Where will you find it?
Saturated fats	butter, cream, palm oil, coconut milk and cream, fried foods and takeaways, fat on meat and skin on chicken, full-fat dairy foods, deli meats and most commercial cakes, pastries, confectionery and biscuits
Monounsaturated fats	olives and olive oil, avocados, peanuts and peanut oil, canola oil, macadamia nuts, hazelnuts, pecan nuts, cashews and almonds
Omega-6 polyunsaturated fats	sunflower, safflower, soya bean, sesame, cottonseed and grape seed oils, pine nuts and Brazil nuts
Omega-3 polyunsaturated fats	oily types of fish (herring, sardine, mackerel, salmon and tuna), walnuts, canola oil, linseeds (flax seeds) and linseed oil, lean red meat and a range of fortified commercial foods
Trans fats	margarines and fat spreads, deep-fried fast food, commercial cakes, pastries, pies and biscuits. (Levels of trans fats in foods may vary according to the country you live in; look for the words 'hydrogenated fats' or 'partially hydrogenated fats' on food labels)

It's likely that around 75 per cent of the salt you eat comes from processed foods. So simply avoiding salt in cooking or at the table is not enough.

cheese, or margarine spreads made from vegetable oils. (If you have high cholesterol, consider choosing a margarine made with plant sterols, which have cholesterol-lowering properties; refer to page 23 for more information).

Cut down on salt

Like high cholesterol, having high blood pressure increases your risk of CVD, and having both at once increases the risk even further. So, it's important that you keep your blood pressure in check at the same time you address your cholesterol levels. Losing weight, drinking less alcohol, being active and eating more fruit and vegetables will all help, as will cutting down on salt.

It's likely that around 75 per cent of the salt you eat comes from processed foods. So simply avoiding salt in cooking or at the table is not enough. To get your salt intake down to healthier levels, take care with what you bring home from the supermarket. Look for reduced-salt or no-added-salt varieties of the regular foods you buy, such as margarine spreads, tinned tomatoes, tomato paste, tomato sauce, cracker biscuits, peanut butter, cheese, bread, cooking stocks and sauces.

Drink alcohol in moderation

Research suggests that moderate alcohol consumption may help protect your heart and blood vessels. It doesn't appear to matter what you drink provided it is alcoholic. Beer, spirits, white wine or red, they all do a similar job—raising good HDL and keeping your blood flowing freely. Red wine with its antioxidants may offer a little extra benefit, but when all is said and done choose what you enjoy most and keep your intake modest. That means consuming

If you find it hard to stop at just one or two drinks try to:

o reduce your thirst with water or diet drinks before you drink alcohol

o choose low alcohol beer

o alternate alcoholic and non-alcoholic drinks

o dilute alcoholic drinks such as wine with soda, or a beer with diet lemonade.

You only need a weight loss of around five to ten per cent to make a positive difference to your cholesterol and overall health.

no more than two standard drinks on one day and having two or more alcohol-free days each week.

Unfortunately, alcohol is a double-edged sword. Loaded with kilojoules, it's not good for your weight and too much raises your blood pressure and triglycerides—all of which increase your risk of heart disease. In excess, alcohol is also responsible for liver disease, some forms of cancer and early death by misadventure. For these reasons, if you don't already drink, don't start just to lower your risk of cardiovascular disease.

Balance your kilojoules

Strategies to stop weight gain are essential in any heart-friendly eating plan and the most important of these are portion and kilojoule control. The sums to support this are simple; eat too much food and kilojoules and you put on weight, eat less food and kilojoules and you lose weight—or at the very least you won't gain. There are no special foods or ways of eating that will change this basic equation. Physical activity is the only factor you can add to tip the balance in your favour.

Cutting back on your kilojoules means focusing on foods that give you more for less—foods with more nutrients but less kilojoules. Give foods like potato chips (crisps), commercial cakes, pastries and biscuits (cookies), sweets, soft drinks (soda) and high-fat savoury crackers the flick, and eat more fruit, vegetables, wholegrain breads and cereals, lean meat, fish, nuts and seeds.

Watching the total amount of fat you eat also makes it easier to balance your kilojoules. A no-fat diet is no good for lowering cholesterol (it's the balance of good fats and bad fats that counts) or losing weight for that matter (it just makes your diet unpalatable and hard to maintain). However, eating less saturated

Most of the foods richest in antioxidant ability are also rich in colour. Think of berries, citrus, cherries, plums, spinach and other green leafy vegetables, broccoli, red capsicum and beetroot. Other antioxidant-rich foods include tea, red wine, dark chocolate, extra virgin olive oil, nuts and herbs.

fat will cut many unhealthy and surplus kilojoules out of your diet. Re-visit our tips for cutting back on saturated fat on page 14 to make sure you target the right ones.

Controlling portion sizes is another way to consume fewer kilojoules. Try eating only the recommended serve of your cereal at breakfast—1⅓ cups of ready-to-eat cereal, ½ cup of natural muesli or 1 cup of cooked porridge—use a smaller sized plate or bowl for meals, or order an entrée-sized meal if you're planning to indulge in dessert when eating out. If you want a second helping choose another serve of salad or vegetables rather than meat, pasta or rice. Another trick to keeping portions in check is to divide up your plate, allowing a quarter of the plate for your protein, a quarter for your carbohydrate and the remaining half for salad or vegetables.

Choosing your carbohydrates wisely also helps with portion control. Select higher fibre, low-GI carbohydrates like grainy bread, pasta, oat-based breakfast cereals, sweet potato, corn, legumes and temperate fruits. Their slower digestion and absorption will keep you feeling fuller and satisfied for longer and make you less likely to snack before your next meal. Their soluble fibre also helps lower your blood cholesterol.

You only need a weight loss of around five to ten per cent to make a positive difference to your cholesterol and overall health.

If you need more help with your weight and diet plan, visit a dietitian. They can help you with a heart-friendly eating plan to help you get and keep the kilos off.

Increase the soluble fibre in your diet by adding psyllium husks or oat, barley or rice bran to your breakfast cereal or baking. Additionally, make sure you eat plenty of fruit, vegetables and legumes.

The power foods

Seek out antioxidants

Free radicals cause damage to your body—known as oxidation—which contributes to ageing and disease. When LDL cholesterol is oxidized by free radicals it becomes stickier and more likely to take part in the process of atherosclerosis, and this makes it more dangerous. You can help prevent LDL cholesterol oxidation by making sure you eat plenty of foods rich in antioxidants. These are natural chemicals found in food that protect your body from free radical damage. Some antioxidants are also vitamins and minerals (for example vitamins C and E and the mineral selenium), while others are naturally-occurring phytochemicals (plant chemicals), such as flavonoids, catechins and anthocyanins.

Although it's not fully understood why, it seems that antioxidants are more effective when consumed from food sources than they are when taken in supplement form, so don't rely on tablets or capsules for your antioxidants. In any case, which is more appealing, a bowl of fresh berries or a supplement pill?

Enjoy more fruits and vegetables

Research reveals that people who eat the most plant foods are among the healthiest and longest living of all. Packed with nutrition, plant foods tend to be low in kilojoules compared to animal foods, so are a great choice when you need to control your weight.

With most being rich in cholesterol-lowering soluble fibre and sterols, fruits and vegetables are also packed with heart-protective

Don't forget nuts and seeds. Once considered off limits for anyone wanting a healthier diet, nuts and seeds have now been given the thumbs up. Although they're high in fats and kilojoules, they're also rich in fibre, healthy fats and heart-protective nutrients like vitamin E, folate, magnesium and copper, and the fats they contain are healthy ones.

vitamins, minerals and antioxidants. Eat by the rainbow to get maximum benefit from your fruit and vegetables: choose at least two serves of fruit and five serves of vegetables each day, selecting the brightest and most colourful types.

Legumes are another important plant food. Whether fresh, dried or canned, legumes (for example, beans, split peas, chickpeas and lentils) are excellent sources of soluble fibre and low in saturated fat. Legumes have a low GI and are rich in heart-friendly antioxidants that protect cholesterol from the oxidative damage that makes it more likely to clog up your arteries.

To reap the health rewards of legumes, incorporate them into at least a couple of meals a week. They make a great vegetarian alternative in curries (chickpeas) and Mexican dishes (kidney beans) but also serve up well at breakfast. You can also try cutting back the meat a little and adding them to stews and soups or using them to lower the GI of meals containing grains like rice and couscous.

Regularly eating a small handful of unsalted nuts or seeds as a snack or added to salad, pasta or breakfast cereal is a good habit for a healthier heart and may even help lower your total cholesterol, LDL cholesterol and triglyceride levels. If you need to lose weight, you'll be reassured to know that studies show people who eat nuts regularly are more likely than those who don't to be a healthy weight, and that two serves a week are not associated with weight gain.

Eat more fibre

Fibre is your friend when you need to get cholesterol down, but unfortunately many of us don't consume the recommended 25–30 grams a day.

Two types of fibre exist in food—soluble and insoluble. Both offer you plenty of health benefits, but it's soluble fibre that directly affects blood cholesterol. Found in oats, barley, psyllium, legumes and some fruit and vegetables, soluble fibre forms a gel-like substance in your intestine that binds up cholesterol and stops your body absorbing it.

Foods made from the whole of the grain—known as wholegrain foods—are also rich in fibre (both soluble and insoluble), low in GI and packed with essential nutrients and antioxidants. This combination of attributes is believed responsible for the ability of wholegrains to help reduce the risk of

CVD, weight problems, some forms of cancer, and type 2 diabetes.

Get the most from these heart-friendly foods by making at least half of your six daily servings of grain and cereal foods wholegrain. For even better results, choose wholegrains every time.

The term 'wholegrain' can be confusing, since it doesn't just apply to 'whole' grains like brown rice and whole-wheat—foods can undergo some processing and still retain the important components of the wholegrain. Boost your daily serves of wholegrain foods by:

○ using wholemeal (whole-wheat) flour instead of white
○ snacking on whole-wheat crackers or popcorn
○ enjoying oats, natural muesli or whole-wheat cereals at breakfast
○ choosing wholegrain or wholemeal breads
○ trying brown rice or barley as a change from white rice
○ choosing wholemeal rather than white pasta

Eat more fish

Fish, especially oily fish, contain healthy polyunsaturated fats known as long chain omega-3s. Omega-3 fats are essential to our health and must be consumed in our diets. Amongst other effects, they protect the cardiovascular system by lowering triglycerides, keeping the heart beating regularly (preventing arrhythmias), maintaining the elasticity of the blood vessels, lessening the risk of blood clots (by keeping the blood more free flowing), and calming inflammation.

To benefit most from omega-3, include oily fish in your diet at least twice a week. Highest concentrations of omega-3 can be found in sardines, salmon, mackerel, tuna, trevally, trout, pilchards and flathead. All fish, even the oily varieties, are low in saturated fat and are a healthy choice at any meal.

It makes no difference if your fish is fresh or canned. The convenience of canned fish makes it perfect for busy lives and those who don't live near the sea. Take care to avoid fish packed in brine (the extra salt may lead to an increase in your blood pressure). Instead, look for canned fish packed in spring water and check the label for those with the most omega-3.

Up your oats

Oats have a proven record for lowering cholesterol thanks to their content of a soluble fibre known as beta glucan. But don't eat just any oats (though they are all good for you). Go for the slower cooking, old-fashioned varieties such as traditional, steel-cut or Scotch oats, which have a lower GI and more beta glucan than quick-cooking and instant varieties.

Consider plant sterols

Plant sterols are found naturally in plant-based foods such as vegetable oils, legumes, fruit, nuts and seeds. By reducing the amount of cholesterol your body absorbs from your intestine, plant sterols ultimately lower blood cholesterol. A typical Western diet won't contain enough plant sterols to make a difference to blood cholesterol, but one that includes foods enriched with plant sterols will.

Depending upon where in the world you live, you may be able to buy margarine spreads, milk, yoghurt and even breakfast cereals enriched with plant sterols. For blood cholesterol benefits you need to eat 2–3 g of plant sterols every day, which usually equates to three servings of sterol-enriched food, but check product packaging to be sure.

Sterol-enriched foods can't be expected to take the place of a healthy diet low in saturated fat. However, the weight of evidence is behind them and heart associations around the world recommend plant sterol-enriched foods be considered as part of a cholesterol lowering diet. However, take care to include at least one serve of an orange-coloured fruit or vegetable such as carrots, pumpkin (winter squash), apricots, mangoes or rockmelon (cantaloupe) in your diet every day while using plant sterols, because they may deplete your body's betacarotene levels.

Final words on lifestyle choices

Despite the fact that this is a cookbook, advice about lowering cholesterol and improving heart health is not complete without mentioning the importance of a healthy lifestyle. Giving up smoking and becoming more physically active are essential for keeping your heart—and the rest of your body—healthy.

Even if you don't become physically active until middle age, every extra hour of exercise you participate in has been estimated

Consider these ways to be more physically active:

o invest in a pedometer and work towards more steps (or 7,500–10,000 steps a day if you are up to the challenge)

o take the stairs rather than the elevator or escalator

o park a little further away from the entrance to your work or the shopping mall

o walk to get the newspaper rather than taking the car

o get up to turn the TV off rather than using the remote

o make a regular date with a friend to go for a walk

o hop on your bike and go for a ride or invest in an exercise bike—you can get at least 30–60 minutes of exercise just watching your favourite TV show

o join a water aerobics group—this is good if you have joint problems or are very overweight

o take up a physical hobby like line dancing, yoga, swimming, tennis or golf

o enjoy active weekends with family and friends: go to the park for a picnic and a game of football or Frisbee, go walking or take a visit to the city for some sight-seeing.

Taking up the lifestyle challenge offers impressive results: within just one year of quitting smoking, heart disease risk drops by 50 per cent.

to have the potential to increase your life expectancy by two hours. Continuing to smoke means a heart attack is much more likely for you than for someone who doesn't smoke, and so too are other forms of cardiovascular disease and many other serious health issues.

Taking up the lifestyle challenge offers impressive results: within just one year of quitting smoking, heart disease risk drops by 50 per cent, and if you are overweight but fit thanks to being a regular exerciser, your risk of early death is significantly lower than that of your equally heavy but unfit peers. What's more, those that have the most to gain from moving more are those who are currently doing the least.

Contact your local quit-smoking service to start the ball rolling toward going smoke free. These services can give you the best advice about when and how to quit plus support and motivation to keep you going once you're on your way.

Before tackling your fitness regimen discuss your plans with your doctor. This is especially important if you haven't exercised regularly for a while or have health problems. When you've received the all-clear aim to build up to 30 minutes of moderate intensity activity on most, if not all days of the week. (Moderate intensity means you're breathing hard, but you can still chat with a friend).

If you are new to the whole exercise thing, consider a few sessions with a personal trainer or exercise physiologist. They can design you a program that suits your personal health needs best.

Your 30 minutes of activity doesn't have to be continuous. Research shows three lots of 10-minute sessions offers similar benefits to one 30-minute session. Thirty minutes is the bare minimum you need for health. If you are up to it, and can do more, then there are only greater health benefits to gain. To lose weight you need to do at least 60 minutes of exercise a day.

How to use this book

The tested recipes in this book have been selected to offer you a range of heart-healthy meals and snacks that can be enjoyed by everyone. Switching the whole family to healthier eating means everyone benefits—especially children. The exception to this rule is that children under 2 years of age should consume full-fat dairy foods. Once they're older they can enjoy the same reduced-fat dairy foods the rest of the family use.

This book contains recipes for everyday meals as well as special occasions, and all aim for less saturated fat. To further enhance the health benefits of these recipes we've included low-salt, high-fibre, low-GI and wholegrain ingredients wherever possible. We've also included plenty of heart-protective foods such as oats, legumes, nuts, brightly coloured fruits and vegetables, and fish, so you get the most for your heart and blood vessels from each recipe.

Disclaimer

The information in this book is intended to provide people with high cholesterol, and people who care for them, with general advice about healthy low-cholesterol eating (accurate at the time of printing).

This advice may not be sufficient for some people with multiple or serious health problems. It is not intended to replace any advice given to you by a qualified doctor or other mainstream health professional. It is important that high cholesterol is diagnosed by a doctor, using standard diagnostic tests (such as blood tests). Neither the author nor the publishers can be held responsible for claims arising from the inappropriate use or incorrect interpretation of any of the dietary advice described in this book.

Breakfast

nutrition per serve   Energy **1525 kJ (364 Cal)** Fat **0.8 g** Saturated fat **0.1 g**
Protein **11.2 g** Carbohydrate **73.2 g** Fibre **6.6 g** Cholesterol **2 mg** Sodium **58 mg**

Mixed berry couscous

185 g (6½ oz/1 cup) instant couscous

500 ml (17 fl oz/2 cups) unsweetened apple and blackcurrant juice

1 cinnamon stick

250 g (9 oz/2 cups) raspberries

255 g (9 oz/1⅔ cups) blueberries

250 g (9 oz/1⅔ cups) strawberries, hulled and halved

2 tsp lime or lemon zest, plus extra,

to serve

1 tbsp finely shredded mint

200 g (7 oz) low-fat plain or fruit-flavoured yoghurt

2 tbsp pure maple syrup

1 Put the couscous in a bowl. Pour the apple and blackcurrant juice into a small saucepan and add the cinnamon stick. Bring to the boil, then remove from heat and pour over couscous. Cover with plastic wrap and leave to stand for 5 minutes, or until all liquid has been absorbed. Remove cinnamon stick. Refrigerate.

2 Separate the couscous grains with a fork, add the berries, lime zest and mint, and gently fold through. Spoon the mixture into 4 bowls. Top with a large dollop of plain or fruit-flavoured yoghurt and drizzle with the maple syrup. Serve chilled.

Prep time 10 minutes + standing
+ refrigeration time
Cooking time 5 minutes
Serves 4

Muesli boost

30 g (1 oz/⅓ cup) flaked almonds

200 g (7 oz/2 cups) rolled (porridge) oats

60 g (2¼ oz/1 cup) processed bran cereal

40 g (1½ oz/⅓ cup) rye flakes

40 g (1½ oz/¼ cup) pepitas (pumpkin seeds)

2 tbsp sunflower seeds

1 tbsp linseeds (flax seeds)

90 g (3¼ oz/¾ cup) sultanas (golden raisins)

185 g (6½ oz/1 cup) chopped dried apricots

90 g (3¼ oz/½ cup) chopped dried pear

low-fat honey-flavoured yoghurt or skim milk, to serve

1 Put the rolled oats, processed bran cereal, rye flakes, pepitas, sunflower seeds and linseeds in a bowl, then stir well to combine. Add the sultanas, apricots and pears as well as the toasted almonds.

2 Serve with low-fat honey-flavoured yoghurt or skim milk if you prefer.

Prep time 10 minutes

Cooking time 5 minutes

Serves 6

nutrition per serve   Energy 1277 kJ (305 Cal) Fat 4.5 Saturated fat 0.8 g
Protein 10.3 g Carbohydrate 52.8 g Fibre 5.5 g Cholesterol 4 mg Sodium 55 g

Bircher muesli

300 g (10½ oz/3 cups) rolled
    (porridge) oats

250 ml (9 fl oz/1 cup) low-fat milk

90 g (3¼ oz/⅓ cup) low-fat plain
    yoghurt

100 ml (3½ fl oz) orange juice

3 tbsp sugar

125 g (4½ oz/½ cup) low-fat plain
    yoghurt, extra

2 apples, grated

2 cups mixed seasonal fresh fruit
    (banana, peach, apricot, melon,
    apple, strawberries)

honey, to serve (optional)

1 Put the oats, milk, yoghurt, orange juice and sugar in a
bowl and mix together well.

2 Cover and refrigerate for 4 hours, or overnight. Serve
with the extra yoghurt, grated apple and fresh fruit of
your choice. Drizzle with a little honey, if desired.

Prep time time: 15 minutes +
4 hours refrigeration
Cooking time time: Nil
Serves 6

Red fruit salad with berries

Syrup

55 g (2 oz/¼ cup) caster (superfine)
  sugar

125 ml (4 fl oz/½ cup) unsweetened
  apple and blackcurrant juice

1 star anise

1 tsp finely chopped lemon rind

250 g (9 oz/1⅔ cups) strawberries,
  hulled and halved

155 g (5½ oz/1 cup) blueberries

155 g (5½ oz/1¼ cups) raspberries,
  mulberries or other red berries

250 g (9 oz/1¼ cups) pitted cherries

5 small red plums, about 250 g
  (9 oz), stones removed and
  quartered

low-fat yoghurt, to serve (optional)

1 To make the syrup, put the sugar, juice, star anise,
lemon rind and 125 ml (4 fl oz/½ cup) water in a small
saucepan. Bring to the boil over medium heat, stirring
to dissolve the sugar. Boil the syrup for 3 minutes,
then set aside to cool for 30 minutes. When cool, strain
the syrup.

2 Mix the fruit together in a large bowl and pour on the
syrup. Mix well to coat the fruit in the syrup and
refrigerate until cooled. Serve the fruit dressed with a
little syrup and the yoghurt.

Prep time 5 minutes +
30 minutes cooling +
30 minutes refrigeration
Cooking time 5 minutes
Serves 6

nutrition per serve   Energy **1242 kJ (297 Cal)** Fat **3.7 g** Saturated fat **0.6 g**
Protein **6 g** Carbohydrate **59 g** Fibre **4.7 g** Cholesterol **0 mg** Sodium **10 g**

Porridge with stewed rhubarb

Dry porridge mix

600 g (1 lb 5 oz/6 cups) rolled (porridge) oats

55 g (2 oz/½ cup) rolled rice flakes

60 g (2¼ oz/½ cup) rolled barley

60 g (2¼ oz/½ cup) rolled rye

30 g (1 oz/¼ cup) millet flakes

Stewed rhubarb

350 g (12 oz) rhubarb, trimmed and washed

100 g (3½ oz/½ cup) soft brown sugar

¼ tsp ground mixed spice

low-fat yoghurt, to serve

Prep time 15 minutes
Cooking time 30 minutes
Serves 4

1 Put all the porridge ingredients in a large bowl and mix together well. The dry mix makes about 8 cups or enough for 16 serves. Store in a large airtight container for up to 2 months.

2 To make enough porridge for 4 serves, put 2 cups porridge mixture in a saucepan with 1.25 litres (44 fl oz/5 cups) water. Bring to the boil, then reduce the heat and simmer, stirring frequently, over a medium heat for 15 minutes, or until the porridge is thick. If it is too thick, add a little skim milk or water.

5 Meanwhile, to make the stewed rhubarb, chop the rhubarb into 2 cm (¾ in) lengths. Put in a saucepan with the sugar, mixed spice and 250 ml (9 fl oz/1 cup) water. Slowly bring to the boil, stirring to dissolve the sugar, then reduce the heat and simmer for 10 minutes, stirring often. Serve hot or cold with the porridge.

nutrition per serve   Energy **630 kJ (150 Cal)** Fat **0.2 g** Saturated fat **0 g**
Protein **1.4 g** Carbohydrate **35 g** Fibre **3.7 g** Cholesterol **0 mg** Sodium **13 mg**

Poached fruit with whole spices

1 orange

1 lemon

250 ml (9 fl oz/1 cup) unsweetened apple juice

6 whole cardamom pods, lightly crushed

6 whole cloves

1 cinnamon stick

375 g (13 oz) dried-fruit medley

3 tbsp soft brown sugar

Prep time 10 minutes + 1 hour soaking

Cooking time 15 minutes

Serves 8

1 Peel 3 large strips of orange rind, avoiding too much white pith. Peel the lemon rind into thick strips. Cut half the orange and lemon rinds into thin strips.

2 Put the apple juice, whole spices and thick strips of rind in a large saucepan with 750 ml (26 fl oz/3 cups) water and bring to the boil. Add the dried fruit. Remove from the heat and set aside for 1 hour.

3 Return to the heat, add the brown sugar and thin strips of rind and cover. Cook over low heat for 5 minutes, or until soft. Remove the fruit with a slotted spoon. Simmer the juice for another 5 minutes, or until reduced and thickened slightly. Serve the fruit warm or cold drizzled with juice.

nutrition per slice   Energy 1119 kJ (267 Cal) Fat 6.4 g Saturated fat 0.9 g
Protein 7.3 g Carbohydrate 43.6 g Fibre 3.6 g Cholesterol 16 mg Sodium 348 mg

Banana bread with maple ricotta

80 ml (2½ oz/⅓ cup) strong coffee

125 g (4½ oz/⅔ cup) soft brown sugar

1 egg

1 egg white

3 tbsp canola oil

1 tsp vanilla extract

3 ripe bananas, mashed

125 g (4½ oz/1 cup) plain flour

250 g (9 oz/2 cups) self-raising flour

½ tsp baking powder

1 tsp ground ginger

½ tsp ground nutmeg

1 tsp ground cinnamon

1 tsp bicarbonate of soda

200 g (7 oz) low-fat ricotta cheese

2 tbsp maple syrup

fresh berries, to serve

1   Preheat the oven to 170°C (325°F/Gas 3). Lightly grease a 22 x 12 cm (8½ x 4½ in) loaf tin and line the base with baking paper. Heat the coffee in a small saucepan over low heat, add the brown sugar and stir until the sugar has dissolved.

2   Put egg, egg white, oil and vanilla in a bowl and beat until just combined. Add coffee mixture and banana.

3   Sift the flours, baking powder, ginger, nutmeg, cinnamon and bicarbonate of soda onto the mixture and stir gently to combine—do not overbeat. Spoon the mixture into the prepared loaf tin. Bake for 50 minutes, or until a skewer comes out clean when inserted into the centre. Leave in the tin for 10 minutes before turning out onto a wire rack to cool completely.

4   Combine the ricotta and maple syrup in a small bowl. Cut the banana bread into thick slices and serve with the maple ricotta and fresh berries.

Prep time 10 minutes

Cooking time 55 minutes

Makes 10–12 slices

nutrition per serve   Energy 1350 kJ (323 Cal) Fat 5.9 g Saturated fat 2 g
Protein 13.3 g Carbohydrate 49.5 g Fibre 8 g Cholesterol 53 mg Sodium 368 g

Oaty buckwheat pancakes

Berry sauce

55 g (2 oz/¼ cup) sugar

2 tsp lemon juice

250 g (9 oz/2 cups) raspberries

40 g (1½ oz/⅓ cup) buckwheat flour

100 g (3½ oz/⅔ cup) wholemeal
  (whole-wheat) flour

1½ tsp baking powder

25 g (1 oz/¼ cup) rolled (porridge)
  oats

1 egg yolk

375 ml (13 fl oz/1½ cups) buttermilk

3 egg whites

olive or canola oil spray

extra raspberries, to serve

Prep time 15 minutes

Cooking time 40 minutes

Serves 4

1 To make the sauce, put the sugar, lemon juice and
60 ml (2 fl oz/¼ cup) water in a saucepan over medium
heat and bring to the boil. Add the raspberries and cook
over low heat for 3 minutes. Cool, then purée in a food
processor or blender for 10 seconds.

3 Sift the flours into a bowl and return the husks to the
bowl. Add the baking powder and rolled oats and
combine. Make a well in the centre. Combine the egg
yolk and buttermilk and add to the dry ingredients all
at once. Stir to form a smooth batter. Whisk the egg
whites until firm peaks form, then fold into the batter.

4 Heat a frying pan over medium heat and spray with oil.
Pour 60 ml (2 fl oz/1/4 cup) batter into pan and swirl to
form a 10 cm (4 in) circle. Cook for 1–2 minutes, or
until bubbles appear on the surface. Turn and cook for
1–2 minutes, or until light brown.

5 Transfer to a plate and keep warm. Repeat to make
8 pancakes. Serve with the berry sauce and raspberries.

Corn cakes with tomato salsa

Tomato salsa

2 tbsp diced red onion

2 firm tomatoes, seeded and diced

½ Lebanese (short) cucumber,
   seeded and diced

2 tbsp flat-leaf (Italian) parsley,
   chopped

1 tbsp olive oil

1 tbsp white vinegar

4 fresh corn cobs or 425 g (15 oz) tin
   corn kernels, drained

2 spring onions (scallions), finely
   chopped

2 eggs, lightly beaten

155 g (5½ oz/1¼ cups) self-raising
   flour

185 ml (6 fl oz/¾ cup) low-fat milk

olive oil spray

1 To make the tomato salsa, put the red onion, tomato, cucumber and parsley in a bowl. Season with freshly ground black pepper, then add the oil and vinegar and toss together well to coat.

2 If using fresh corn, remove the kernels by cutting down the length of the cob with a sharp knife. Put the kernels in a small bowl with the spring onion and combine.

3 Whisk together the egg, self-raising flour and milk in a bowl until smooth. Fold in corn and spring onion mixture and season with freshly ground black pepper.

4 Heat a frying pan over medium heat and spray with oil. Working in batches, drop ¼ cup of batter per corn cake into the pan and allow enough space for spreading. Cook over medium heat for 2 minutes, or until golden. Turn over and cook for a further 1–2 minutes, or until golden. Repeat with the remaining batter to make 12 corn cakes.

5 To serve, stack three corn cakes on individual plates and top with some tomato salsa.

Prep time 15 minutes
Cooking time 15 minutes
Serves 4

nutrition per serve   Energy **583 kJ (139 Cal)** Fat **0.5 g** Saturated fat **0 g**
Protein **2.6 g** Carbohydrate **28.1 g** Fibre **5.2 g** Cholesterol **0 mg** Sodium **13 mg**

Fruit frappé

10 dried apricot halves

205 g (7¼ oz/1½ cups) raspberries

1 banana, roughly chopped

1 mango, chopped

500 ml (17 fl oz/2 cups) orange juice

1 tbsp mint leaves

6 ice cubes

Prep time 5 minutes + 10 minutes
soaking
Cooking time Nil
Serves 4

1 Put the dried apricots in a heatproof bowl. Cover with 60 ml (2 fl oz/¼ cup) boiling water and soak for 10 minutes, or until plump. Drain, then roughly chop.

2 Put the chopped apricots, raspberries, banana, mango, orange juice, mint leaves and ice cubes in a blender, and blend until thick and smooth.

nutrition per serve   Energy **1399 kJ (334 Cal)** Fat **8.5 g** Saturated fat **2 g**
Protein **20.8 g** Carbohydrate **39.5 g** Fibre **6.1 g** Cholesterol **188 mg** Sodium **572 mg**

Mushrooms with scrambled eggs

4 field mushrooms

olive oil spray

4 roma (plum) tomatoes, halved

3 tbsp balsamic vinegar

4 eggs, lightly beaten

4 egg whites, lightly beaten

3 tbsp low-fat milk

2 tbsp snipped fresh chives

8 thick slices wholegrain bread

1 Trim the mushroom stalks to 2 cm (¾ in) below the
cap. Wipe the mushrooms with paper towels to remove
any dirt and grit.

2 Spray both sides of the mushrooms with the oil and
place on a non-stick baking tray with the tomatoes.
Drizzle the mushrooms and tomatoes with the
balsamic vinegar, then season with freshly ground black
pepper and place under a medium grill (broiler) for
10–15 minutes, or until tender.

Prep time 15 minutes
Cooking time 15 minutes
Serves 4

3 Meanwhile, put the eggs, egg whites, milk and chives in
a bowl and whisk together to combine. Pour the
mixture into a non-stick frying pan and cook over a low
heat for 2–3 minutes, or until the egg begins to set,
then gently stir with a wooden spoon to scramble.

4 Toast the wholegrain bread until golden brown, then
cut on the diagonal. Serve with the mushrooms, tomato
and scrambled eggs.

nutrition per serve
Energy Energy 680 kJ (162 Cal) Fat 0.6 g Saturated fat 0.2 g
Protein 10.3 g Carbohydrate 27 g Fibre 3.2 g Cholesterol 8 mg Sodium 109 mg

Raspberry and banana smoothie

625 ml (21½ fl oz/2½ cups) skim milk

2 bananas

125 g (4½ oz/1 cup) raspberries

185 g (6½ oz/¾ cup) low-fat vanilla yoghurt

1 tbsp oat bran

1 Put the milk in a covered container in the freezer for 30 minutes to make it very cold. It should be cold but not icy.

2 Peel and chop the bananas and put them in a blender. Add the raspberries, yoghurt, oat bran and 250 ml (9 fl oz/1 cup) of the milk. Blend for 30 seconds, or until smooth.

3 Add the remaining milk and blend for a further 30 seconds, or until combined.

4 Pour into four glasses and serve immediately.

Prep time 5 minutes + 30 minutes chilling

Cooking time Nil

Serves 4

nutrition per serve   Energy **714 kJ (171 Cal)** Fat **0.5 g** Saturated fat **0 g**
Protein **3.2 g** Carbohydrate **33.7 g** Fibre **8 g** Cholesterol **0 mg** Sodium **156 mg**

Carrot cocktail

10–12 carrots, quartered lengthways

125 ml (4 fl oz/½ cup) pineapple juice

125 ml (4 fl oz/½ cup) unsweetened orange juice

1–2 tsp honey, to taste

8 ice cubes

1 Using the plunger, push the carrot pieces through a juicer.

2 Combine the carrot juice with the pineapple juice, orange juice, honey and ice cubes in a jug and serve.

Prep time 10 minutes
Cooking time Nil
Serves 2

nutrition per serve Energy **984 kJ (235 Cal)** Fat **0.8 g** Saturated fat **0 g**
Protein **4.6 g** Carbohydrate **47.9 g** Fibre **5 g** Cholesterol **0 mg** Sodium **38 g**

Peach and rockmelon juice

½ **rockmelon**

4 **peaches**

600 ml (21 fl oz) **unsweetened orange juice**

12 **ice cubes**

1 tbsp **lime juice**

Prep time 10 minutes
Cooking time Nil
Serves 2

1 Peel the rockmelon, remove the seeds and roughly chop the flesh into bite-sized pieces. Cut a cross in the base of each peach. Put them in a heatproof bowl and cover with boiling water. Leave for 1–2 minutes, then remove with a slotted spoon, cool slightly and peel. Halve, remove the stone, and chop the flesh into bite-sized pieces.

2 Put the fruit in a blender with the orange juice and ice cubes, and blend until smooth. If the juice is too thick, add a little iced water. Stir in the lime juice and serve immediately.

nutrition per serve Energy **936 kJ (224 Cal)** Fat **1.9 g** Saturated fat **0.3 g**
Protein **9.4 g** Carbohydrate **37.9 g** Fibre **4.5 g** Cholesterol **0 mg** Sodium **78 mg**

Summer fruit soy smoothie

1 banana

4 peaches, chopped

175 g (6 oz/¾ cup) apricot and mango soy yoghurt or
   vanilla soy yoghurt

1 tbsp oat bran

1 tsp natural vanilla extract

625 ml (21½ fl oz/2½ cups) reduced-fat plain soy milk or
   vanilla soy milk

1 tbsp maple syrup, optional

extra peach slices, to serve

ice cubes, to serve

1 Put the banana, peach, yoghurt, oat bran, vanilla
extract and 250 ml (9 fl oz/1 cup) of the soy milk in a
blender and blend for 30 seconds, or until smooth.

2 Add the remaining soy milk and blend for a further
30 seconds, or until combined. Taste for sweetness and
add the maple syrup, if using. Put the ice and extra
peach slices in four glasses, pour in the smoothie and
serve immediately.

Prep time 10 minutes
Cooking time Nil
Serves 4

Snacks and starters

nutrition per serve   Energy 314 kJ (75 Cal) Fat 2.2 g Saturated fat 0.3 g
Protein 4 g Carbohydrate 8.7 g Fibre 2.7 g Cholesterol 1 mg Sodium 60 mg

White bean and chickpea dip

3 slices wholegrain bread

3 tbsp low-fat milk

400 g (14 oz) tinned cannellini
beans, drained and rinsed

300 g (10½ oz) tin chickpeas,
drained and rinsed

2 spring onions (scallions), finely
chopped

90 g (3¼ oz/⅓ cup) low-fat plain
yoghurt

2 tbsp lemon juice

2 tsp finely grated lemon zest

1 tbsp chopped parsley

2 tsp chopped oregano

1 tbsp olive oil

vegetable crudités, to serve

1 Remove the crusts from the bread, put the bread in a
bowl and drizzle with the milk. Leave for 2 minutes,
then mash with your fingertips until very soft.

2 Using a food processor or blender, process the
cannellini beans, chickpeas, soaked bread, spring onion,
yoghurt, lemon juice, zest, herbs and oil until combined
but retaining some texture. Season well with freshly
ground black pepper. Serve at room temperature with
the vegetable crudités.

Prep time 10 minutes

Cooking time Nil

Serves 12

Pâté with tortilla crisps

1 tsp olive oil

1 small onion, chopped

2 garlic cloves, crushed

300 g (10½ oz) flat mushrooms, wiped clean and chopped

4 tbsp white wine or water

80 g (2¾ oz/1 cup) fresh wholemeal (whole-wheat) breadcrumbs

2 tbsp finely chopped thyme, plus extra to serve

2 tbsp chopped flat-leaf (Italian) parsley

1 tbsp lemon juice

4 large tortillas, about 20 cm (8 in) in diameter, each cut into 8 wedges

olive oil spray

1 Heat the oil in a large, deep frying pan. Add the onion and garlic and cook, stirring, for 2 minutes without browning. Add the mushrooms and wine. Cook, stirring for 1 minute, then cover and simmer for 5 minutes, stirring once or twice. Remove the lid and increase the heat to evaporate any liquid. Cool.

2 Put the mushroom mixture, breadcrumbs, herbs and lemon juice in a food processor or blender. Process until smooth and season well with freshly ground black pepper. Spoon into a serving bowl. Cover and refrigerate for at least 1 hour to allow the flavours to develop.

3 Preheat the oven to 180°C (350°F/Gas 4). Put the tortilla wedges on a large baking tray and lightly spray with the oil. Lightly sprinkle with freshly ground black pepper. Bake for 8 minutes, or until crisp. Serve the pâté with the tortilla crisps.

Prep time 15 minutes + 1 hour refrigeration

Cooking time 20 minutes

Serves 4–6

Sweet potato and red lentil dip

2 tsp olive oil

1 small red onion, finely chopped

1 garlic clove, crushed

1 tsp grated fresh ginger

1 tbsp Thai red curry paste

**200 g (7 oz) tinned reduced-salt
diced tomatoes**

**125 g (4½ oz/½ cup) red lentils,
drained and rinsed**

**375 ml (13 fl oz/1½ cups) reduced-
salt chicken stock**

**250 g (9 oz) orange sweet potato,
roughly chopped**

Prep time 20 minutes + cooling
time
Cooking time 50 minutes
Serves 6–8

1 Heat the oil in a saucepan over medium heat and cook
the onion for 2 minutes, or until softened. Add the
garlic, ginger and curry paste and stir for 30 seconds.

2 Add the tomatoes, lentils and stock to the pan. Bring to
the boil, then reduce the heat to low, cover and simmer,
stirring often, for 30 minutes, or until the mixture
thickens and the lentils have softened but are still
intact. Spoon the mixture into a bowl and refrigerate
until cold.

3 Meanwhile, put the sweet potato in a steamer and
cover with a lid. Sit the steamer over a wok or saucepan
of boiling water and steam for 15 minutes, or until
tender. Transfer to a bowl, cool and mash roughly with
a fork.

4 Carefully stir the mashed sweet potato into the lentil
mixture with a fork. Season to taste with freshly ground
black pepper. Serve with pitta bread wedges, savoury
crackers or crusty bread for dipping.

nutrition per serve   Energy **487 kJ (116 Cal)** Fat **4.8 g** Saturated fat **0.6 g**
Protein **4.8 g** Carbohydrate **11.7 g** Fibre **4.1 g** Cholesterol **<1 mg** Sodium **184 mg**

Beetroot hummus

500 g (1 lb 2 oz) beetroot (beets), trimmed

1 tbsp olive oil

1 large onion, chopped

1 tbsp ground cumin

400 g (14 oz) tinned chickpeas, drained and rinsed

1 tbsp tahini

90 g (3 ¼ oz/⅓ cup) low-fat plain yoghurt

3 garlic cloves, crushed

60 ml (2 fl oz/¼ cup) lemon juice

125 ml (4 fl oz/½ cup) reduced-salt vegetable stock

Turkish bread, to serve (optional)

1 Scrub beetroot well. Bring a large saucepan of water to the boil and cook beetroot for 40 minutes or until soft and cooked through. Drain and cool before peeling.

2 Meanwhile, heat the oil in a frying pan over medium heat and cook the onion for 2 minutes, or until soft. Add the cumin and cook for a further 1 minute, or until fragrant.

3 Chop the beetroot and put in a food processor or blender with the onion mixture, chickpeas, tahini, yoghurt, garlic, lemon juice and stock, and process until smooth and thoroughly combined. Spoon the hummus into a serving bowl and serve with Turkish bread.

Prep time 15 minutes
Cooking time 40 minutes
Serves 8

nutrition per serve Energy **938 kJ (224 Cal)** Fat **12 g** Saturated fat **1.4 g**
Protein **18.1 g** Carbohydrate **9.5 g** Fibre **5.2 g** Cholesterol **0 mg** Sodium **93 mg**

Tabouleh with soy grits

150 g (5½ oz) flat-leaf (Italian)
    parsley

180 g (6½ g/1 cup) soy grits

2 tbsp chopped mint

1 small red onion, cut into thin
    wedges

3 tomatoes, chopped

400 g (14 oz) tinned chickpeas,
    drained and rinsed

3 tbsp lemon juice

2 tbsp extra virgin olive oil

Lebanese or pitta bread, to serve
    (optional)

1 Remove all the parsley leaves from the stalks, roughly chop and put in a large serving bowl.

2 Put the soy grits in a heatproof bowl and pour in 170 ml (5½ fl oz/⅔ cup) boiling water. Leave to soak for 3 minutes, or until all the water has been absorbed.

3 Add the soy grits to the parsley, along with the mint, onion, tomato and chickpeas. Drizzle with the lemon juice and olive oil. Season well with freshly ground black pepper and toss together. Serve with Lebanese or pitta bread.

Prep time 20 minutes + soaking
Cooking time Nil
Serves 6–8

nutrition per serve   Energy **279 kJ (67 Cal)** Fat **2.5 g** Saturated fat **0.4 g**
Protein **1.4 g** Carbohydrate **8.8 g** Fibre **1.9 g** Cholesterol **2 mg** Sodium **240 mg**

Smoky eggplant tapenade

1 large eggplant (aubergine), about 500 g (1 lb 2 oz)

310 g (11 oz/2 cups) pitted kalamata olives

5 anchovy fillets in brine, drained

35 g (1¼ oz/¼ cup) capers, rinsed and squeezed dry

3 garlic cloves, finely chopped

1 small handful flat-leaf (Italian) parsley

1 small handful basil

1 small handful oregano

1 tbsp lemon juice

1 tbsp extra virgin olive oil

crackers or vegetable crudités, to serve (optional)

1 Preheat the barbecue chargrill plate to high. Cook the
eggplant, turning frequently, for 15–20 minutes, or
until the skin is black all over and the flesh is soft.
Remove from the heat. When cool enough to handle,
cut off the stem, peel off the skin and roughly chop
the eggplant flesh.

2 Put olives, anchovies, capers, garlic, parsley, basil,
oregano, lemon juice and oil in a small blender. Process
for 10–15 seconds, or until roughly chopped.

3 Add the chopped eggplant and blend in 3-second bursts
for 15 seconds, or until the tapenade has a medium–
smooth consistency with a little texture. Season with
freshly ground black pepper and transfer to a serving
bowl. Serve with crackers or vegetable crudités.

Prep time 20 minutes
Cooking time 20 minutes
Serves 10

San choy bau

4 dried Chinese mushrooms

3 tsp canola oil, for cooking

30 g (1 oz/¼ cup) slivered almonds, chopped

125 g (4 oz) water chestnuts, drained and finely chopped

1 carrot, finely chopped

4 spring onions (scallions), finely chopped

250 g (9 oz) lean minced (ground) pork

4 coriander (cilantro) roots, finely chopped

1 tbsp grated fresh ginger

12 lettuce leaves

hoisin sauce, to serve (optional)

Sauce

1 tbsp reduced-salt soy sauce

1 tbsp lime juice

1 tsp sesame oil

15 g (½ oz/¼ cup) chopped fresh coriander (cilantro) leaves

2 tbsp chopped fresh mint

1 Soak the mushrooms in a small bowl of hot water for 10 minutes, or until softened. Discard the tough stems and finely chop the mushroom caps.

2 To make the sauce, combine the soy sauce, lime juice, sesame oil, coriander leaves and mint in a small jug.

3 Heat the wok until very hot, add 1 teaspoon of the oil and swirl around to coat the side. Add the almonds, water chestnuts, carrot and spring onion to the wok and stir-fry for 1 minute, or until they are lightly cooked but not browned—they should still be crisp. Remove from the wok and set aside.

4 Reheat the wok and add the remaining 2 teaspoons of canola oil. Stir-fry the minced pork, coriander root, ginger and mushrooms over medium–high heat for 2–3 minutes, or until the pork changes colour, but do not overcook the pork or it will be tough. Add the sauce and stir to combine. Return the vegetable mixture to the wok and stir-fry for 1–2 minutes, or until heated through and the mixture is well combined.

5 Spoon the pork mixture into the lettuce leaves and dollop with the hoisin sauce, to taste. Serve with hoisin sauce for dipping.

Prep time 25 minutes + 10 minutes soaking
Cooking time 10 minutes

Prawns with bean and corn salad

400 g (14 oz) tin cannellini beans, drained and rinsed

300 g (10½ oz) tin chickpeas, drained and rinsed

310 g (11 oz) tin corn kernels, drained and rinsed

1 tsp grated lime zest

2 tbsp chopped coriander (cilantro) leaves

500 g (1 lb 2 oz) raw large prawns (shrimp)

2 tbsp lemon juice

1 tbsp sesame oil

2 garlic cloves, crushed

2 tsp grated fresh ginger

olive or canola oil spray

lime quarters, to serve

Prep time 10 minutes + 3 hours marinating
Cooking time 5 minutes
Serves 4

1 Combine cannellini beans, chickpeas and corn kernels in a large bowl. Stir through the lime zest and coriander.

2 Peel the prawns, leaving the tails intact. Gently pull out the dark vein from each prawn back, starting at the head end.

3 To make the marinade, combine the lemon juice, sesame oil, garlic and ginger in a small bowl. Add the prawns and gently stir to coat them in the marinade. Cover and refrigerate for at least 3 hours.

4 Heat a barbecue hotplate until hot. Spray the hotplate with oil, then cook the prawns for 3–5 minutes, or until pink and cooked through. Brush frequently with marinade while cooking. Serve immediately with the bean mixture and wedges of lime.

Vietnamese rice paper rolls

50 g (1¾ oz) dried rice vermicelli

200 g (7 oz) frozen soy beans

**16 square (15 cm/6 in) rice paper
wrappers**

1 zucchini (courgette), julienned

**1 Lebanese (short) cucumber,
julienned**

1 carrot, grated

20 g (¾ oz/1 cup) mint

**100 g (3½ oz) firm tofu, cut
into 1 cm (½ in) strips**

Dipping sauce

2 tbsp sweet chilli sauce

2 tbsp lime or lemon juice

2 tsp soft brown sugar

**1 tsp reduced-sodium soy sauce or
tamari**

**2 tbsp chopped coriander (cilantro)
leaves**

1 Soak the vermicelli in hot water for 5 minutes, or until
soft. Drain and cut into 5 cm (2 in) lengths with a pair
of scissors. Bring a saucepan of water to the boil, add
the soy beans and cook for 2 minutes. Drain well.

2 Working with no more than 2 rice paper wrappers at
a time, dip each wrapper in a bowl of warm water for
10 seconds to soften. Drain and then lay out on a flat
work surface.

3 Put a small amount of rice vermicelli on the bottom
third of a wrapper, leaving a 2 cm (¾ in) border either
side. Top with a little zucchini, cucumber, carrot, soy
beans, mint and 2 strips of tofu. Keeping the filling
compact and neat, fold in both sides and roll up tightly.
Seal with a little water, if necessary. Cover with a damp
cloth and repeat with the remaining rice paper
wrappers and filling ingredients.

4 To make the dipping sauce, combine all the ingredients
with 2 tablespoons water in a small bowl and stir
together well. Serve with the rice paper rolls.

Prep time 40 minutes + 5 minutes
soaking
Cooking time 2 minutes
Serves 4

nutrition per serve Energy **1301 kJ (311 Cal)** Fat **13.5 g** Saturated fat **2.9 g**
Protein **7.3 g** Carbohydrate **37.1 g** Fibre **5.5 g** Cholesterol **1 mg** Sodium **130 mg**

Sweet potatoes with salsa

4 x 200 g (7 oz) orange sweet potatoes

1 red onion, finely chopped

1 avocado, finely chopped

1 tbsp lemon juice

130 g (4½ oz) tin corn kernels, drained

½ red capsicum (pepper), finely chopped

1 tbsp sweet chilli sauce

low-fat plain yoghurt, to serve

1 Preheat the oven to 200°C (400°F/Gas 6). Prick the sweet potatoes a few times with a skewer. Bake on an oven rack for 50 minutes, or until cooked through.

2 Meanwhile, put the onion, avocado, lemon juice, corn and capsicum in a bowl and mix together well. Stir in the chilli sauce and season to taste with freshly ground black pepper.

3 Make a deep cut along the top of each cooked sweet potato. Divide the topping among the sweet potatoes and add a dollop of low-fat plain yoghurt.

Prep time 15 minutes
Cooking time 50 minutes
Serves 4

Soups and salads

Jerusalem artichoke soup

1 tbsp olive oil

1 onion, roughly chopped

1 leek, white part only, chopped

1 celery stalk, chopped

2 garlic cloves, chopped

800 g (1 lb 12 oz) Jerusalem
    artichokes, cut into 5 cm (2 in)
    pieces

2 potatoes, about 250 g (9 oz), cut
    into 5 cm (2 in) pieces

1 tsp freshly grated nutmeg

250 ml (9 fl oz/1 cup) reduced-salt
    chicken stock or vegetable stock

500 ml (17 fl oz/2 cups) low-fat milk

2 tbsps finely snipped chives

Prep time 20 minutes

Cooking time 35 minutes

Serves 4

1 Heat the oil in a large heavy-based saucepan over low
heat. Add the onion, leek, celery and garlic and cook for
2 minutes. Cover and simmer, stirring occasionally, for
5 minutes. Do not allow the vegetables to brown.

2 Add the Jerusalem artichokes, potato and nutmeg and
stir to combine. Cook for 2 minutes, then add the stock,
250 ml (9 fl oz/1 cup) water and 250 ml (9 fl oz/1 cup)
of the milk. Bring to the boil, cover and cook for
20 minutes, or until the vegetables are tender.

3 Remove the saucepan from the heat. Set aside to cool
slightly. Using a food processor or blender, process the
soup for 10 seconds, or until roughly puréed. Season
well with freshly ground black pepper. Stir in the
remaining milk and half the chives and gently reheat
the soup.

4 Ladle the soup into four bowls and sprinkle with the
remaining chives and some freshly ground black pepper.

Split pea soup

1 tbsp olive oil

1 large brown onion, chopped

1 large carrot, cut into
    1 cm (½ in) cubes

1 large celery stalk, cut into
    1 cm (½ in) cubes

2 bay leaves

1 tbsp finely chopped thyme

6 garlic cloves, finely chopped

440 g (15½ oz/2 cups) yellow split
    peas

1 litre (35 fl oz/4 cups) reduced-salt
    chicken stock

60 ml (2 fl oz/¼ cup) lemon juice

grainy bread, to serve (optional)

mixed-leaf salad, to serve (optional)

1 Heat the oil in a large saucepan over medium heat. Add the onion, carrot and celery, and cook for 4–5 minutes, or until starting to brown. Add the bay leaves, thyme and garlic, and cook for 1 minute.

2 Stir in the split peas, then add the chicken stock and 1 litre (35 fl oz/4 cups) water. Cook for 1 hour 20 minutes, or until the split peas and vegetables are soft. Stir often during cooking to prevent the soup from sticking to the bottom of the pan, and skim any scum from the surface. Add a little extra water if the soup is too thick.

3 Remove the soup from the heat and discard the bay leaves. Stir in the lemon juice and season with freshly ground black pepper. Serve with grainy bread and a mixed-leaf salad.

Prep time 20 minutes
Cooking time 1 hour 30 minutes
Serves 6–8

nutrition per serve   Energy **722 kJ (173 Cal)** Fat **8 g** Saturated fat **2.5 g**
Protein **8.5 g** Carbohydrate **14.3 g** Fibre **4.5 g** Cholesterol **3 mg** Sodium **359 mg**

Alsace mushroom soup

10 g (¼ oz) dried porcini mushrooms

1 tbsp olive oil

1 onion, roughly chopped

4 French shallots, chopped

1 large potato (about 185 g/6½ oz), chopped

1 celery stalk, chopped

2 garlic cloves, chopped

1 small red chilli, seeded and chopped

175 g (6 oz) flat mushrooms, roughly chopped

175 g (6 oz) Swiss brown mushrooms, roughly chopped

500 ml (17 fl oz/2 cups) reduced-salt chicken stock or vegetable stock

2 large thyme sprigs

1–2 tsp lemon juice, to taste

90 g (3¼ oz/⅓ cup) extra-light sour cream, to serve

2 tbsp finely chopped flat-leaf (Italian) parsley, to serve

1 tbsp grated lemon zest, to serve

1 Put the porcini mushrooms in a small bowl and pour 250 ml (9 fl oz/1 cup) hot water over them. Set aside to soften for 10 minutes.

2 Meanwhile, heat the oil in a large heavy-based saucepan. Add the onion, shallots, potato, celery, garlic and chilli. Stir for 2 minutes to coat the vegetables in the margarine. Reduce the heat, cover and simmer, stirring occasionally, for 5 minutes. Do not allow the vegetables to brown.

3 Add the fresh mushrooms to the saucepan and cook, stirring, for 2–3 minutes. Add the stock, 250 ml (9 fl oz/1 cup) water, thyme sprigs and porcini mushrooms with their soaking water. Slowly bring to the boil over low heat, then reduce the heat and simmer, covered, for 15 minutes. Discard the thyme sprigs. Set aside to cool slightly.

4 Using a food processor or blender, process the soup for 15–20 seconds, or until roughly puréed. The soup should still have texture. Add the lemon juice, to taste, and season well with freshly ground black pepper. Gently reheat the soup and ladle into warm bowls. Top with a spoonful of the sour cream and sprinkle with the parsley and lemon zest.

Prep time 25 minutes +
10 minutes soaking

Cooking time 30 minutes

Serves 4

nutrition per serve   Energy **952 kJ (228 Cal)** Fat **6.7 g** Saturated fat **3.3 g**
Protein **22.5 g** Carbohydrate **16.3 g** Fibre **5.7 g** Cholesterol **65 mg** Sodium **91 mg**

Scotch broth

1 kg (2 lb 4 oz) lamb shanks, cut in half through the bone (ask your butcher to do this)

3 onions, chopped

3 turnips, chopped

2 carrots, chopped

1 tbsp black peppercorns

110 g (3¾ oz/½ cup) pearl barley

1 carrot, diced, extra

2 onions, finely chopped, extra

2 turnips, diced, extra

1 leek, white part only, chopped

1 celery stalk, diced

chopped flat-leaf (Italian) parsley, to serve

Prep time 40 minutes + 1 hour soaking + overnight refrigeration
Cooking time 3 hours 35 minutes
Serves 8

1 To make the stock, put the lamb shanks, onion, turnip, carrot, peppercorns and 2 litres (70 fl oz/8 cups) water in a large saucepan. Bring to the boil, reduce the heat to medium and simmer, covered, for 3 hours. Skim the surface as required.

2 Remove the shanks and any meat that has fallen off the bones and cool slightly. Remove the meat from the bones and finely chop, then cover and refrigerate. Strain the stock, discarding the vegetables. Cool the stock and refrigerate overnight, or until the fat has set on top and can be spooned off. Cover the barley with water and soak for 1 hour, then drain.

3 Put the stock in a large pan and gently reheat. Add the barley, extra carrot, onion and turnip, and the leek and celery. Bring to the boil, reduce the heat and simmer for 30 minutes, or until the barley and vegetables are just cooked. Return the meat to the pan and simmer for 5 minutes. Season well with freshly ground black pepper and serve with the parsley.

nutrition per serve   Energy **603 kJ (144 Cal)** Fat **5 g** Saturated fat **0.6 g**
Protein **4.3 g** Carbohydrate **17.4 g** Fibre **5.5 g** Cholesterol **0 mg** Sodium **99 mg**

Beetroot and red capsicum soup

6 beetroot (beets), about 600 g
   (1 lb 5 oz) without stems or leaves

1 tbsp olive oil

1 red onion, chopped

1 celery stalk, chopped

1 garlic clove, chopped

1 large red capsicum (pepper),
   chopped

410 g (14½ oz) tin reduced-salt diced
   tomatoes

1 tbsp red wine vinegar

extra-light sour cream or low-fat
   plain yoghurt, to serve (optional)

2 tbsp finely snipped chives, to serve

Prep time 20 minutes

Cooking time 50 minutes

Serves 4

1 Peel the beetroot with a vegetable peeler and cut it into
3 cm (1¼ in) cubes. Put the beetroot in a large saucepan
with 1 litre (35 fl oz/4 cups) water. Slowly bring to the
boil over low–medium heat, then reduce the heat and
simmer for 25–30 minutes, or until the beetroot is
tender when pierced with a fork. Remove about ½ cup
of beetroot cubes, dice finely and set aside.

2 Meanwhile, heat the oil in a large heavy-based saucepan
over medium heat. Add the onion, celery, garlic and
capsicum and stir to coat the vegetables in the oil.
Reduce the heat to low, cover and cook, stirring
occasionally, for 10 minutes. Do not allow the
vegetables to brown. Add the chopped tomatoes and
vinegar and simmer for 10 minutes.

3 Transfer the tomato mixture to the saucepan
containing the beetroot and remove the pan from the
heat. Set aside to cool slightly. Using a food processor or
blender, process the soup for 20–30 seconds, or until
smooth. Season well with freshly ground black pepper.

4 Ladle the soup into four warm bowls and top with a
spoonful of sour cream, the reserved diced beetroot and
the chives.

nutrition per serve   Energy **977 kJ (233 Cal)** Fat **6.2 g** Saturated fat **1.3 g**
Protein **13.5 g** Carbohydrate **27.6 g** Fibre **7.7 g** Cholesterol **1 mg** Sodium **28 mg**

Spiced pumpkin and lentil soup

1 tbsp olive oil

1 large onion, chopped

3 garlic cloves, chopped

1 tsp ground turmeric

½ tsp ground coriander

½ tsp ground cumin

½ tsp chilli flakes

700 g (1 lb 9 oz/4½ cups) pumpkin (winter squash), chopped

125 g (4½ oz/½ cup) tinned red lentils, drained and rinsed

90 g (3¼ oz/⅓ cup) plain low-fat yoghurt, to serve

Prep time 20 minutes
Cooking time 30 minutes
Serves 4

1 Heat the oil in a large saucepan over medium heat. Add the onion and garlic and fry for 5 minutes, or until softened, being careful not to burn the garlic. Add the turmeric, coriander, cumin and chilli flakes and fry, stirring constantly, for 2 minutes.

2 Add pumpkin, red lentils and 1 litre (35 fl oz/4 cups) boiling water. Bring to the boil, then reduce the heat and simmer, covered, for 20 minutes, or until the pumpkin and lentils are tender. Set aside to cool for 5 minutes.

3 Using a food processor or blender, process the soup for 25–35 seconds, or until evenly chopped. Season well with freshly ground black pepper and reheat the soup.

4 Ladle the soup into four bowls, top with a spoonful of the yoghurt and sprinkle with more pepper.

nutrition per serve Energy **1487 kJ (355 Cal)** Fat **4.1 g** Saturated fat **0.6 g**
Protein **13.3 g** Carbohydrate **62.4 g** Fibre **5.9 g** Cholesterol **2 mg** Sodium **234 mg**

Couscous salad

300 g (10½ oz) orange sweet potato, cubed

100 g (3½oz) green beans, halved

350 g (12 oz/2 cups) instant couscous

500 ml (17 fl oz/2 cups) boiling reduced-salt chicken stock

200 g (7 oz) cherry tomatoes, halved

150 g (5½ oz/1 cup) frozen corn kernels, thawed

155 g (5½ oz/1 cup) frozen peas, thawed

1 red capsicum (pepper), chopped

60 g (2¼ oz/1 cup) chopped parsley

25 g (1 oz/½ cup) chopped mint

Dressing

1 garlic clove, crushed

2 tbsp lemon juice

1 tbsp olive oil

1 tsp honey

½ tsp grainy mustard

1 Boil or steam the sweet potato and beans in separate saucepans until tender, then drain. Put the couscous in a large bowl and pour on the boiling stock. Cover and leave for 5 minutes, or until all the liquid has been absorbed. Fluff with a fork to separate the grains.

2 Add sweet potato, beans, tomato, corn, peas, capsicum and herbs to the couscous, and mix together well.

3 Put the garlic, lemon juice, oil, honey and mustard in a bowl, and whisk together. Pour the dressing over the salad and toss well.

Prep time 20 minutes + 5 minutes standing
Cooking time 15 minutes
Serves 6

nutrition per serve

Energy **661 kJ (158 Cal)** Fat **6.8 g** Saturated fat **1.1 g**
Protein **6.2 g** Carbohydrate **15.6 g** Fibre **5.3 g** Cholesterol **0 mg** Sodium **122 mg**

Chickpea and vegetable salad

500 g (1 lb 2 oz) butternut pumpkin (squash), cubed

2 red capsicums (peppers), halved

4 slender eggplants (aubergines), cut in half lengthways

4 zucchini (courgettes), cut in half lengthways

4 onions, quartered

olive oil spray

2 x 300 g (10 oz) tins chickpeas, drained and rinsed

2 tbsp chopped fresh flat-leaf (Italian) parsley

Dressing

3 tbsp lemon juice

2 tbsp olive oil

1 garlic clove, crushed

1 tsp finely chopped thyme

Prep time 25 minutes +
30 minutes standing
Cooking time 40 minutes
Serves 8

1 Preheat the oven to 220°C (425°F/Gas 7). Line 2 baking trays with baking paper and lay out the vegetables in a single layer and spray them with oil.

2 Bake for 40 minutes, or until the vegetables are tender and begin to brown slightly on the edges. Cool. Remove skins from the capsicum if desired. Chop capsicum, eggplant and zucchini into pieces, then put vegetables in a bowl with chickpeas and half the parsley.

3 Whisk together all the dressing ingredients. Season with freshly ground black pepper, then toss with the vegetables. Leave for 30 minutes, then sprinkle with the rest of the parsley.

Herbed pasta and salmon salad

400 g (14 oz) small pasta shells

250 g (9 oz) cherry tomatoes, quartered, or halved, if small

1 large yellow capsicum (pepper), seeded and diced

2 celery stalks, thinly sliced

3 spring onions (scallions), thinly sliced

40 g (1½ oz/¼ cup) pitted green olives in brine, drained and chopped

2 tbsp capers, rinsed and chopped (optional)

200 g (7 oz) smoked salmon, sliced

1 handful basil, finely shredded

3 tbsp finely chopped flat-leaf (Italian) parsley

Dressing

1 tbsp olive oil

1½ tbsps white wine vinegar

1 tsp honey

Prep time 15 minutes
Cooking time 10 minutes
Serves 4–6

1 Cook the pasta in a large saucepan of boiling water for 10 minutes, or until al dente. Rinse under cold water to cool. Drain. Put in a large bowl.

2 To make the dressing, whisk all the ingredients together. Put all the other ingredients into the bowl with the pasta, add the dressing and toss together. Season with freshly ground black pepper and serve.

Tuna and bean salad

100 g (3½ oz) green beans, chopped

400 g (14 oz) tin butterbeans (lima beans), drained and rinsed

425 g (15 oz) tin tuna in spring water, drained

200 g (7 oz) cherry tomatoes, quartered

1 red onion, thinly sliced

100 g (3½ oz) mixed salad leaves

100 g (3½ oz) baby rocket (arugula) leaves

Dressing

1 tbsp extra virgin olive oil

2 tbsp lemon juice

1 tsp honey

1 garlic clove, crushed

2 tbsp chopped dill

1 Steam the green beans until tender, rinse under cold water and drain. Put the green and butterbeans, tuna, tomato and onion in a bowl, and toss well.

2 To make the dressing, whisk all the ingredients together. Pour the dressing over the tuna mixture, cover and refrigerate for 10 minutes.

3 Combine the salad leaves and rocket, and arrange on a salad platter. Top with the tuna mixture and serve.

Prep time 20 minutes +
10 minutes refrigeration
Cooking time 5 minutes
Serves 4

nutrition per serve   Energy **1475 kJ (352 Cal)** Fat **16.7 g** Saturated fat **3.4 g**
Protein **33.4 g;** Carbohydrate **15.9 g** Fibre **2.5 g** Cholesterol **114 mg** Sodium **115 mg**

Chicken and mango salad

Dressing

2 tbsp rice vinegar

3 tsp honey

3 cm (1¼ in) piece ginger, chopped

1 tbsp canola oil

1 tsp sesame oil

125 g (4½ oz) mixed Asian salad
   leaves

1 large mango, thinly sliced

125 g (4½ oz/1 cup) yellow or red
   cherry tomatoes, halved

1/2 small red onion, sliced into thin
   wedges

1 cold barbecued chicken, fat and
   skin removed, meat shredded

30 g (1 oz/¾ cup) snow pea
   (mangetout) sprouts, trimmed

2 tsp toasted sesame seeds

Prep time 15 minutes
Cooking time nil
Serves 4

1 To make the dressing, put the vinegar, honey and ginger
in a mini food processor or blender and process in
3-second bursts for 20 seconds, or until finely chopped.
With the motor running, slowly pour in the oils and
blend for 20 seconds, or until thick and creamy.

2 Arrange the salad leaves on individual plates and top
with the mango, tomatoes, onion, chicken and snow
pea sprouts. Drizzle with the dressing and sprinkle with
the sesame seeds. Serve immediately.

Pesto beef salad

1 large red capsicum (pepper)

1 large yellow capsicum (pepper)

olive or canola oil spray

100 g (3½ oz) lean beef fillet steak, trimmed

125 g (4½ oz) penne

100 g (3½oz) button mushrooms, quartered

nutrition per serve
Energy **1028 kJ (246 Cal)** Fat **9.5 g** Saturated fat **1.7 g** Protein **12.3 g** Carbohydrate **25.7 g** Fibre **3.6 g** Cholesterol **17 mg** Sodium **20 mg**

Pesto

½ **bunch basil (about 50 g/1¾ oz leaves)**

2 **garlic cloves, chopped**

2 **tbsp pepitas (pumpkin seeds)**

1 **tbsp olive oil**

2 **tbsp orange juice**

1 **tbsp lemon juice**

Prep time 30 minutes + 5 minutes standing

Cooking time 25 minutes

Serves 4

1 Cut the capsicums into large flat pieces, removing the seeds and membrane. Put, skin side up, under a hot grill (broiler) until blackened. Leave covered with a tea towel (dish towel) until cool, then peel away the skin and chop the flesh.

2 Heat a frying pan over medium heat and spray with oil, then cook the steak over high heat for 3–4 minutes on each side. Remove and leave for 5 minutes before cutting into thin slices.

3 To make the pesto, finely chop the basil, garlic and pepitas in a food processor. With the motor running, add the oil, orange and lemon juice. Season well with freshly ground black pepper.

4 Meanwhile, cook the pasta in a large saucepan of boiling water for 10 minutes, or until al dente. Drain well and toss with pesto in a large bowl. Add capsicum pieces, steak slices and mushroom quarters to penne and toss to distribute evenly. Serve immediately.

nutrition per serve   Energy **988 kJ (236 Cal)** Fat **6.7 g** Saturated fat **0.8 g**
Protein **6.8 g** Carbohydrate **35.5 g** Fibre **2.6 g** Cholesterol **0 mg** Sodium **9 mg**

Vietnamese rice noodle salad

200 g (7 oz) dried vermicelli

80 g (3 oz/½ cup) crushed roasted peanuts

10 g (¼ oz/½ cup) Vietnamese mint, torn

15 g (½ oz/½ cup) coriander (cilantro) leaves

½ red onion, cut into thin wedges

1 green mango, julienned

1 Lebanese (short) cucumber, halved lengthways and thinly sliced on the diagonal

Lemongrass dressing

125 ml (4 fl oz/½ cup) lime juice

1 tbsp shaved palm sugar or brown sugar

3 tbsp seasoned rice vinegar

2 lemongrass stems, finely chopped

3 makrut (kaffir lime) leaves, finely shredded

1 Put the rice vermicelli in a bowl and cover with boiling water. Leave for 10 minutes or until soft, then drain, rinse under cold water and cut into short lengths.

2 Put the vermicelli, peanuts, mint, coriander, onion, mango and cucumber in a large bowl and toss together.

3 To make the dressing, put all the ingredients in a jar with a lid and shake.

4 Toss salad and dressing and refrigerate for 30 minutes before serving.

Prep time 20 minutes +
10 minutes standing + 30 minutes
refrigeration
Cooking time nil
Serves 4–6

nutrition per serve Energy **1021 kJ (244 Cal)** Fat **5.4 g** Saturated fat **2.1 g**
Protein **31.4 g** Carbohydrate **14.5 g** Fibre **3.5 g** Cholesterol **84 mg** Sodium **144 mg**

Tandoori lamb salad

250 g (9 oz/1 cup) low-fat plain yoghurt

2 garlic cloves, crushed

2 tsp grated fresh ginger

2 tsp ground turmeric

2 tsp ground garam masala

¼ tsp paprika

2 tsp ground coriander

500 g (1 lb 2 oz) lean lamb fillets

4 tbsp lemon juice

1½ tsp chopped coriander leaves (cilantro)

1 tsp chopped mint

150 g (5 oz) mixed salad leaves

1 large mango, cut into strips

2 Lebanese (short) cucumbers, julienned

1 Mix the yoghurt, garlic, ginger, dried herbs and spices in a bowl, and toss with the lamb to thoroughly coat. Cover and refrigerate overnight.

2 Grill (broil) the lamb on a foil-lined baking tray under high heat for 7 minutes each side, or until the marinade starts to brown. Set aside for 5 minutes before serving.

3 Mix the lemon juice, coriander leaves and mint then season with freshly ground black pepper. Toss with the salad leaves, mango and cucumber, then arrange on plates. Slice the lamb and serve over the salad.

Prep time 20 minutes + overnight marinating
Cooking time 15 minutes
Serves 4

nutrition per serve   Energy **989 kJ (236 Cal)** Fat **7.7 g** Saturated fat **2 g**
Protein **23.9 g** Carbohydrate **15.7 g** Fibre **3.7 g** Cholesterol **76 mg** Sodium **150 mg**

Chicken and sweet potato salad

4 roma (plum) tomatoes, quartered
lengthways

300 g (10½ oz) eggplant (aubergine),
quartered lengthways

olive oil spray

500 g (1 lb 2 oz) orange sweet potato,
cut into 2 cm (¾ in) slices

1 large red onion, sliced into thin
wedges

1 barbecued chicken

2 tbsp chopped coriander (cilantro)
leaves

2–3 tbsp balsamic vinegar

2 handfuls rocket (arugula)

Prep time 30 minutes
Cooking time 50 minutes
Serves 6

1 Preheat the oven to 200°C (400°F/Gas 6). Put the tomatoes and eggplant on a large, non-stick baking tray, spray with a little oil and season with freshly ground black pepper. Bake for 25–30 minutes.

2 Meanwhile, steam the sweet potato for 15 minutes, or until just tender. Put in a large bowl with the tomato and eggplant.

3 Lightly spray a small non-stick frying pan with oil, add the onion and cook over a low heat for 6 minutes, or until golden. Set aside.

4 Remove the skin and bones from the chicken and discard. Cut the chicken meat into bite-sized pieces and add to the vegetables with the coriander and 1 tablespoon balsamic vinegar. Toss gently. Put the rocket on a platter, then the chicken mixture and top with onion. Drizzle with remaining balsamic vinegar to taste. Serve with thick slices of wholegrain bread.

Main meals

Fish tikka

Marinade

250 g (9 oz/1 cup) low-fat plain
   yoghurt

2 spring onions (scallions), finely
   chopped

1 tbsp grated fresh ginger

2 garlic cloves, crushed

2 tbsp lemon juice

1 tsp ground coriander

1 tbsp garam masala

1 tsp paprika

1 tsp chilli powder

2 tbsp no-added-salt tomato paste
   (concentrated purée)

nutrition per serve
Energy **1171 kJ (280 Cal)** Fat **9 g** Saturated fat **4.3 g**
Protein **33.2 g** Carbohydrate **13.4 g** Fibre **3 g** Cholesterol **104 mg** Sodium **263 mg**

500 g (1 lb 2 oz) skinless firm white fish fillets (such as flake, sea bream, snapper, grouper or orange roughy)

2 onions, each cut into 8 chunks

2 small green or red capsicums (peppers), each cut into 8 chunks

boiled rice, to serve (optional)

lemon wedges, to serve

Yoghurt Dressing

50 g (1 3/4 oz/about 1/3 cup) peeled, diced Lebanese (short) cucumber

1 tbsp chopped coriander (cilantro) leaves

250 g (9 oz/1 cup) low-fat plain yoghurt

Prep time 25 minutes +
1 hour marinating
Cooking time 6 minutes
Serves 4

1 Mix all the marinade ingredients together in a shallow non-metallic dish long enough and deep enough to hold eight long metal skewers.

2 Cut the fish into 24 bite-sized chunks. On each skewer, thread 3 fish pieces, 2 onion pieces and 2 capsicum pieces, alternating them as you go. Turn the skewers about in the marinade so that all the fish and vegetables are well coated. Cover and marinate in the refrigerator for at least 1 hour, or overnight if convenient.

3 Mix the yoghurt dressing ingredients together in a small bowl and set aside.

4 Heat the grill (broiler) to its highest setting. When the grill is very hot, lift the skewers out of the marinade and grill for 5–6 minutes, or until the fish is firm and slightly charred. Serve with the yoghurt dressing and lemon wedges.

nutrition per serve
Energy **1656 kJ (396 Cal)** Fat **12.1 g** Saturated fat **1.6 g** Protein **34.4 g** Carbohydrate **31.9 g** Fibre **8.9 g** Cholesterol **78 mg** Sodium **151 mg**

Blue-eye cod in chermoula

Chermoula

1½ tbsp cumin seeds

2 tsp coriander seeds

1 tbsp sweet paprika

pinch cayenne pepper

2 large handfuls coriander (cilantro), chopped

1 large handful flat-leaf (Italian) parsley, chopped

4 large garlic cloves, crushed

2 tbsp olive oil

4 tbsp lemon juice

4 x 150 g (5½ oz) blue-eye cod steaks or other firm white fish steaks

700 g (1 lb 9 oz) small new potatoes

500 g (1 lb 2 oz) zucchini (courgette), thickly sliced

115 g (4 oz) fresh baby corn

Prep time 20 minutes + 1 hour marinating

Cooking time 20 minutes

Serves 4

1 To make the chermoula, place the cumin and coriander seeds, paprika and cayenne pepper in a small, dry frying pan and toast for 1 minute over a medium heat, or until fragrant. Put in a spice grinder, or use a mortar and pestle, and grind to a fine powder. Put in a food processor with the coriander leaves, parsley, garlic, oil and lemon juice. Season with freshly ground black pepper and process until well combined.

2 Put the fish in a flat, non-metallic dish and pour over the chermoula. Toss to coat well, cover and marinate in the refrigerator for 1 hour.

3 Bring a large saucepan of water to the boil and cook the potatoes for 10–12 minutes, or until cooked when tested with a skewer. Steam the zucchini and corn for 3 minutes, or until just cooked.

4 Meanwhile, remove the fish from the chermoula, reserving the liquid. Heat a chargrill plate or barbecue over a high heat and cook the fish for 2–3 minutes on each side, basting with the remaining chermoula. Serve immediately with the potatoes, zucchini and corn.

nutrition per serve

nutrition per serve   Energy **1063 kJ (254 Cal)** Fat **4.5 g** Saturated fat **1.1 g**
Protein **30.8 g** Carbohydrate **15.2 g** Fibre **3.3 g** Cholesterol **83 mg** Sodium **203 mg**

Chicken cacciatore

500 g (1 lb 2 oz) lean chicken breast fillets

plain (all-purpose) flour, for dusting

2 tsp olive oil

2 onions, thinly sliced

2 garlic cloves, finely chopped

2 anchovy fillets in brine, drained and chopped

440 g (15½ oz) tin reduced-salt diced tomatoes

125 ml (4 fl oz/½ cup) dry white wine

3 tbsp no-added-salt tomato paste (concentrated purée)

1 tsp soft brown sugar

6 Kalamata olives, pitted and chopped

chopped fresh flat-leaf (Italian) parsley, to garnish

fusilli pasta or boiled potatoes, to serve (optional)

1 Trim any fat from the chicken and lightly dust the chicken in plain flour. Heat the oil in a large, heavy-based non-stick frying pan and cook the chicken over high heat for 10 minutes, turning until golden and almost cooked. (If the chicken begins to stick, sprinkle with water and reduce the heat.) Remove, drain on paper towels, cover and set aside.

2 Add the onion to the pan with the garlic, anchovies and 1 tablespoon water. Cover and cook for 5 minutes, stirring. Add the tomato, wine, tomato paste, sugar and 200 ml (7 fl oz) water. Bring to the boil, then reduce the heat and simmer for 20 minutes. Season with freshly ground black pepper.

3 Return the chicken and juices to the pan. Add the olives and simmer for 5 minutes, or until the chicken is heated through. Garnish with parsley. Serve with fusilli pasta or boiled potatoes.

Prep time 25 minutes

Cooking time 40 minutes

Serves 4

nutrition per serve   Energy **1757 kJ (420 Cal)** Fat **5.3 g** Saturated fat **1.3 g**
Protein **48.7 g** Carbohydrate **36.3 g** Fibre **10.9 g** Cholesterol **96 mg** Sodium **169 mg**

Coral trout with gremolata

8 vine-ripened tomatoes, halved

12 garlic cloves, unpeeled

2 tbsp balsamic vinegar

1 tbsp soft brown sugar

olive or canola oil spray

750 g (1 lb 10 oz) new potatoes

300 g (10½ oz) asparagus, trimmed

4 x 200 g (7 oz) coral trout fillets or
  firm white fish fillets

Gremolata

3 handfuls flat-leaf (Italian) parsley,
  finely chopped

2 tsp lemon zest

2 garlic cloves, finely chopped

Prep time 20 minutes
Cooking time 55 minutes
Serves 4

1 Preheat the oven to 200°C (400°F/Gas 6). Line a large baking tray with baking paper. Put the tomatoes, cut-side-up, on the prepared tray. Scatter around the garlic cloves. Pour over the combined balsamic vinegar and sugar. Spray lightly with the oil. Bake the tomatoes and garlic for 30 minutes, or until softened. Remove the garlic after 15 minutes and baste the tomatoes with the balsamic vinegar and sugar. Squeeze out the soft garlic from the cloves and add to the mushy tomatoes.

2 Combine the gremolata ingredients in a small bowl.

3 Bring a large saucepan of water to the boil. Cook the potatoes for 12 minutes, or until cooked when tested with a skewer. Drain. Steam the asparagus for 3–4 minutes, or until just tender.

4 Pat the fish dry with paper towels. Spray a large, non-stick frying pan with oil and lightly spray the fish. Cook the fish for 3–4 minutes on each side, or until browned on both sides and just cooked through.

5 To serve, pile the tomato and garlic onto serving plates. Top with the fish fillets and spoon over some gremolata. Serve with the boiled new potatoes and steamed asparagus to the side.

Jungle pork curry

Curry paste

8–10 large dried red chillies

1 tbsp shrimp paste

1 tsp white pepper

1 lemongrass stem, white part only, sliced

5 red Asian shallots, sliced

5 garlic cloves, crushed

1 tbsp finely chopped galangal

2 tsp finely grated fresh ginger

2 small coriander (cilantro) roots, chopped

nutrition per serve
Energy **1896 kJ (453 Cal)** Fat **6.5 g** Saturated fat **1.4 g**
Protein **38.7 g** Carbohydrate **54.8 g** Fibre **5.5 g** Cholesterol **121 mg** Sodium **561 mg**

2 tsp canola oil

1 garlic clove, finely chopped, extra

500 g (1 lb 2 oz) lean pork fillet, thinly sliced

500 ml (17 fl oz/2 cups) reduced-salt chicken stock

½ tbsp reduced-salt soy sauce

85 g (3 oz) Thai apple eggplants (aubergines), quartered, or Thai pea eggplants (aubergines)

100 g (3½ oz) snake (yard-long) beans, cut into 3 cm (1¼ in) lengths

60 g (2¼ oz/¼ cup) sliced bamboo shoots

4 makrut (kaffir lime) leaves, torn

1 small handful Thai basil leaves, plus extra to serve

1 long red chilli, seeded and julienned

boiled basmati rice, to serve

1 To make the curry paste, soak the dried chillies in boiling water for 10 minutes. Drain and chop. Wrap the shrimp paste in foil and toast in a hot wok for 1 minute on each side. Remove from the foil and put the shrimp paste in a food processor or blender with the chopped chilli and remaining paste ingredients. Process until smooth. Add a little water if necessary to form a smooth paste.

2 Heat a wok over medium heat, add the oil and swirl to coat. Add the garlic and 4 tablespoons of the curry paste and cook, stirring, for 1–2 minutes, or until fragrant. Add the pork and stir-fry for 2–3 minutes, or until browned. Pour in the stock and soy sauce, stir to combine, then bring to the boil. Add the eggplant, snake beans, bamboo shoots and lime leaves, reduce the heat and simmer for 5–8 minutes, or until the vegetables are tender but not soft. Remove from the heat and stir in the basil leaves. Garnish with the chilli strips and extra basil leaves and serve with the rice.

Prep time 30 minutes + 10 minutes soaking
Cooking time 20 minutes
Serves 4

Barbecued pork and broccoli

2 tsp canola oil

1 large onion, thinly sliced

2 carrots, julienned

200 g (7 oz) broccoli, chopped

6 spring onions (scallions),
    diagonally sliced

1 tbsp finely chopped fresh ginger

3 garlic cloves, finely chopped

400 g (14 oz) Chinese barbecued
    pork, thinly sliced and trimmed
    of fat

1 tbsp reduced-sodium soy sauce

2 tbsp mirin

185 g (6½ oz/2 cups) bean sprouts

boiled basmati rice, to serve
    (optional)

1 Heat a wok until very hot, add the oil and swirl it
around to coat the sides. Stir-fry the onion over
medium heat for 3–4 minutes, or until slightly softened.
Add the carrot, broccoli, spring onion, ginger and garlic
and cook for 4–5 minutes, tossing mixture constantly.

2 Increase the heat to high and add the barbecued pork.
Toss constantly until the pork is well mixed with the
vegetables and is heated through. Add the soy sauce
and mirin, and toss until the ingredients are well
coated. (The wok should be hot enough for the sauce to
reduce into a glaze.) Add the bean sprouts and season
with freshly ground black pepper. Serve immediately
with the boiled rice.

Prep time 25 minutes

Cooking time 10 minutes

Serves 4

Lemongrass chicken

**4 lemongrass stems, white part only,
  halved lengthways**

**3 boneless, skinless chicken breasts,
  halved lengthways**

2 tsp sesame oil

2 red chillies, seeded and chopped

**300 g (10½ oz) Chinese broccoli
  (gai larn), halved**

300 g (10½ oz) plain rice noodle rolls

reduced-salt soy sauce, to serve

lime wedges, to serve

1   Arrange the lemongrass in a steamer. Put the chicken
on top, brush with the sesame oil and sprinkle with
chilli. Cover with a lid. Sit the steamer over a wok or
saucepan of boiling water and steam for 5 minutes,
or until half cooked.

2   Put the Chinese broccoli and rice noodle rolls in
another steamer of the same size and sit it on top of
the steamer with the chicken. Cover with a lid and
steam for a further 5 minutes, or until the chicken is
cooked and the broccoli is tender. Cut the chicken into
thick slices and serve with the broccoli, noodle rolls,
small bowls of soy sauce and wedges of lime.

Prep time 15 minutes
Cooking time 10 minutes
Serves 4

Lamb and asparagus stir-fry

300 g (10½ oz) dried mung bean vermicelli

2 tsp green peppercorns, finely chopped

3 garlic cloves, finely chopped

2 tsp canola oil

400 g (14 oz) lean lamb fillets

canola oil spray

1 onion, cut into small wedges

4 tbsp dry sherry

1 green capsicum (pepper), cut into strips

200 g (7 oz) broccoli florets

16 small asparagus spears, trimmed and cut into bite-sized pieces

2 tbsp oyster sauce

garlic chives, cut into short lengths, to garnish

Prep time 35 minutes +

20 minutes marinating +

10 minutes soaking

Cooking time 30 minutes

Serves 4

1 Put the noodles in a large bowl and cover with warm water. Soak for 10 minutes, or until they are translucent. Transfer to a saucepan of boiling water and cook for 15 minutes, or until tender. Rinse under cold water, then drain. Use scissors to cut into shorter lengths.

2 To make the marinade, put the green peppercorns, garlic and oil in a large non-metallic bowl. Add the lamb and toss well to coat. Cover with plastic wrap and marinate for 20 minutes.

3 Trim the lamb and cut into bite-sized pieces. Heat a wok over high heat until slightly smoking. Add the lamb in small batches and stir-fry briefly until browned and just cooked. Remove from the wok and keep warm. Reheat the wok between batches.

4 Reheat the wok, spray with oil and stir-fry the onion and 2 teaspoons of the sherry for 1 minute. Add the capsicum and a pinch of salt. Cover, steam for 2 minutes, add the broccoli, asparagus and the remaining sherry and stir-fry for 1 minute. Cover and steam for 3 minutes, or until the vegetables are just tender. Return the lamb to the pan, add the oyster sauce and stir to combine with the vegetables. Add the noodles and stir through until warmed. Serve garnished with the garlic chives.

nutrition per serve   Energy **2267 kJ (542 Cal)** Fat **11.6 g** Saturated fat **4.1 g**
Protein **60.4 g** Carbohydrate **54.5 g** Fibre **3.5 g** Cholesterol **120 mg** Sodium **308 mg**

Beef in black bean sauce

2 garlic cloves, crushed

2 tsp grated fresh ginger

2 tbsp dry sherry

1 tbsp reduced-salt soy sauce

**750 g (1 lb 10 oz) lean beef rump
    steak**

1 tsp cornflour (cornstarch)

2 tsp canola oil

2 onions, cut into wedges

**1 large green capsicum (pepper), cut
    into strips**

**235 g (8½ oz) tin sliced bamboo
    shoots, drained and rinsed**

**2 tbsp tinned black beans, rinsed
    and chopped**

boiled basmati rice, to serve

Prep time 20 minutes + 1 hour
marinating
Cooking time 30 minutes
Serves 4

1 To make the marinade, combine the garlic, ginger,
sherry and soy sauce in a non-metallic bowl. Trim the
meat, then slice across the grain into long, thin strips.
Add to the marinade and toss to coat well. Cover with
plastic wrap and refrigerate for at least 1 hour, turning
occasionally. Drain the meat, reserving the marinade.

2 Meanwhile, to make the stir-fry sauce, mix the
cornflour and remaining marinade with 2 tablespoons
water until smooth.

3 Heat a wok until very hot, add half the oil and swirl to
coat the sides. Add the meat in small batches and stir-
fry briefly until browned but not cooked through.
Remove from the wok and drain on paper towels.
Reheat the wok between batches.

4 Heat the remaining oil in the wok and swirl to coat the
sides. Add the onion and capsicum and stir-fry over
high heat for 3 minutes, or until the onion is soft. Add
the bamboo shoots and black beans, then cook for
1 minute.

5 Return the meat to the wok along with the stir-fry
sauce and stir-fry over high heat until the meat is
cooked through and the sauce has thickened. Serve
immediately with the rice.

Penne with bacon and ricotta

2 tsp olive oil

4 low-fat back bacon slices (we used 97% fat-free), chopped

2–3 garlic cloves, crushed

1 onion, finely chopped

2 spring onions (scallions), finely chopped

250 g (9 oz/1 cup) low-fat ricotta cheese

3 handfuls basil, finely chopped, plus extra whole leaves, to
　　garnish

325 g (11½ oz) penne

12 cherry tomatoes, halved

1 Heat the oil in a frying pan, add the bacon, garlic, onion
and spring onion and stir over medium heat for
5 minutes, or until cooked. Remove from the heat, stir
in the ricotta and chopped basil and beat until smooth.

2 Cook the pasta in a large saucepan of boiling water for
10 minutes, or until al dente. Just prior to draining the
pasta, add about 250 ml (9 fl oz/1 cup) of the pasta
cooking water to the ricotta mixture to thin the sauce.
Add more water if you prefer an even thinner sauce.
Season with freshly ground black pepper.

3 Drain pasta and stir ricotta sauce and tomato halves
through the pasta. Garnish with extra basil and serve.

Prep time 20 minutes
Cooking time 15 minutes
Serves 4

Prawn kebabs with salsa

Mango salsa

2 tomatoes

1 small just-ripe mango, diced

½ small red onion, diced

1 small red chilli, seeded and finely
  chopped

grated zest and juice of 1 lime

2 tbsp chopped coriander (cilantro)
  leaves

nutrition per serve
Energy **2121 kJ (507 Cal)** Fat **6.3 g** Saturated fat **0.9 g** Protein **38 g** Carbohydrate **69.3 g** Fibre **3.3 g** Cholesterol **226 mg** Sodium **547 mg**

Marinade

2 tbsp clear runny honey

1 small red chilli, seeded and finely chopped

1 tbsp olive oil

grated zest and juice of 2 limes

1 large garlic clove, crushed

2 cm (¾ in) piece fresh ginger, peeled and finely grated

1 tbsp chopped coriander (cilantro) leaves

32 tiger or king prawns (shrimp), peeled and deveined, tails intact

boiled rice, to serve

Prep time 25 minutes +
30 minutes soaking + 2 hours
marinating

Cooking time 5 minutes

Serves 4

1 Before you start cooking, soak eight bamboo skewers in cold water for 30 minutes. While the skewers are soaking, make the salsa. Score a cross in the base of each tomato and put them in a heatproof bowl. Cover with boiling water, leave for 30 seconds, then plunge in cold water and peel the skin away from the cross. Remove the seeds, dice the flesh, saving any juices, and put the tomato with all its juices in a bowl. Mix in the mango, onion, chilli, lime zest, lime juice and coriander.

2 In a small bowl, whisk together the honey, chilli, oil, lime zest, lime juice, garlic, ginger and coriander. Put the prawns in a non-metallic dish, add the marinade and toss well. Cover and refrigerate for 2 or more hours, turning the prawns occasionally.

3 Heat the grill (broiler) to high. Thread 4 prawns onto each skewer and grill for 4 minutes, or until pink and cooked through, turning halfway through cooking and basting regularly with the left-over marinade. Serve at once with the salsa and the rice.

nutrition per serve Energy **1692 kJ (404 Cal)** Fat **7.1 g** Saturated fat **2.1 g**
Protein **26.7 g** Carbohydrate **54.4 g** Fibre **3.1 g** Cholesterol **56 mg** Sodium **516 mg**

Beef with oyster sauce

1½ tsp cornflour (cornstarch)

125 ml (4 fl oz/½ cup) reduced-salt beef stock

1½ tbsp oyster sauce

1 tsp finely crushed garlic

1 tsp caster (superfine) sugar

2 tsp canola oil

350 g (12 oz) lean rump steak, finely sliced

250 g (9 oz) green beans, topped and tailed,
   cut into 5 cm (2 in) lengths

1 small red capsicum (pepper), sliced

60 g (2¼ oz/⅔ cup) bean sprouts

boiled basmati rice, to serve

Prep time 15 minutes
Cooking time 10 minutes
Serves 4

1 Dissolve the cornflour in a little of the stock. Mix with the remaining stock, oyster sauce, garlic and sugar and set aside.

2 Heat the wok until very hot, add the oil and swirl it around to coat the sides. Add the beef in batches and stir-fry over high heat for 2 minutes, or until it browns.

3 Add beans and capsicum and stir-fry another minute.

4 Add the cornflour mixture to the wok and cook until the sauce boils and thickens. Stir in the bean sprouts and serve immediately with the rice.

nutrition per serve Energy **2457 kJ (589 Cal)** Fat **13.7 g** Saturated fat **2.2 g**
Protein **39.6 g** Carbohydrate **63.3 g** Fibre **20.7 g** Cholesterol **65 mg** Sodium **190 mg**

Middle-Eastern chicken

350 g (12 oz/2 cups) burghul (bulgur)

2 skinless chicken breast fillets

2 tsp olive oil

1 red onion, thinly sliced

300 g (10½ oz) tin chickpeas, drained and rinsed

70 g (2½ oz/½ cup) unsalted pistachio kernels

1 tomato, chopped

juice of 1 orange

4 tbsp finely chopped flat-leaf (Italian) parsley

Prep time 15 minutes +
15 minutes soaking
Cooking time 20 minutes
Serves 4

1 Put the burghul in a bowl, cover with water and leave to soak for 15 minutes, or until the burghul has softened. Drain and use clean hands to squeeze dry.

2 Meanwhile, trim the chicken and thinly slice. Heat a large frying pan over high heat, add half the oil and swirl to coat. Add the chicken in batches and stir-fry for 3–5 minutes, or until cooked. Remove from the pan and keep warm. Reheat the pan between batches.

3 Add the remaining oil to the pan and cook the onion, stirring, for 2 minutes, then add the chickpeas, pistachio kernels and tomato. Cook, stirring, for 3–5 minutes, or until chickpeas are warmed through.

4 Pour in the orange juice, return the chicken and its juices to the pan and cook until half the juice has evaporated. Stir in the parsley. Season with freshly ground black pepper and serve with the burghul.

Pasta with meatballs

**500 g (1 lb 2 oz) lean minced
(ground) veal**

1 onion, very finely chopped

4 garlic cloves, finely chopped

1 egg white, lightly beaten

**80 g (2¾ oz/1 cup) fresh
breadcrumbs**

**30 g (1 oz/½ cup) finely chopped
parsley**

**7 g (¼ oz/¼ cup) finely chopped
oregano**

olive oil spray

**1.5 kg (3 lb 5 oz) tomatoes, peeled,
roughly chopped**

2 onions, thinly sliced, extra

**125 g (4½ oz/½ cup) no-added-salt
tomato paste (concentrated
purée)**

½ tsp sugar

350 g (12 oz) penne

mixed-leaf salad, to serve (optional)

1 Combine the minced veal, onion, half the garlic, egg
white, breadcrumbs, two-thirds of the parsley and
1 tablespoon of the oregano. Season well. Mix with
your hands until well combined. Shape into small balls.

2 Heat a frying pan and spray with oil. Cook the
meatballs in three batches over high heat for
4–5 minutes, or until browned, turning constantly.
Remove from the pan.

3 Lightly spray the base of a large, deep non-stick
saucepan with oil. Add the sliced onion and remaining
garlic. Cook over low heat for 2–3 minutes, stirring.
Add 2 tablespoons water, cover and cook for 5 minutes.
Stir in the tomatoes and tomato paste. Simmer, covered,
for 10 minutes, then uncover and simmer gently for
40 minutes. Add the meatballs, and simmer, covered,
for 15–20 minutes, or until just cooked. Add the sugar,
remaining parsley and oregano, and season with freshly
ground black pepper.

4 Cook the pasta in a large saucepan of boiling water for
10 minutes, or until al dente, then drain. Serve with the
hot meatballs and the salad.

Prep time 40 minutes

Cooking time 1 hour 50 minutes

Serves 6

nutrition per serve   Energy **1719 kJ (411 Cal)** Fat **7.5 g** Saturated fat **3.2 g**
Protein **40.4 g** Carbohydrate **39.7 g** Fibre **6.3 g** Cholesterol **53 mg** Sodium **299 mg**

Chicken and vegetable lasagne

500 g (1 lb 2 oz) chicken breast fillets

olive oil spray

2 garlic cloves, crushed

1 onion, chopped

2 zucchini (courgettes), chopped

2 celery stalks, chopped

2 carrots, chopped

300 g (10½ oz) pumpkin (winter squash), diced

2 x 400 g (14 oz) tins reduced-salt diced tomatoes

2 sprigs thyme

2 bay leaves

2 tbsp no-added-salt tomato paste (concentrated purée)

125 ml (4 fl oz/½ cup) dry white wine

2 tbsp chopped basil

500 g (1 lb 2 oz) English spinach

500 g (1 lb 2 oz) low-fat cottage cheese

450 g (1 lb) low-fat ricotta cheese

60 ml (2 fl oz/¼ cup) skim milk

½ tsp ground nutmeg

35 g (1¼ oz/⅓ cup) grated parmesan cheese

300 g (10½ oz) lasagne sheets

1 Preheat the oven to 180°C (350°F/Gas 4). Trim any excess fat from the chicken breasts, then finely mince in a food processor. Heat a large, deep, non-stick frying pan, spray lightly with oil and cook the chicken mince in batches until browned. Set aside. Add the garlic and onion to the pan and cook until softened. Return the chicken to the pan and add the zucchini, celery, carrot, pumpkin, tomato, thyme, bay leaves, tomato paste and wine. Simmer, covered, for 20 minutes. Remove the bay leaves and thyme, stir in the fresh basil and set aside.

2 Shred the spinach and set aside. Mix the cottage cheese, ricotta, skim milk, nutmeg and half the parmesan. Spoon a little of the tomato mixture over the base of a casserole dish and top with a single layer of pasta, top with half the remaining tomato mixture, then the spinach and spoon over half the cottage cheese mixture. Continue with another layer of pasta. Spread remaining tomato mixture then the cottage cheese on top and sprinkle with parmesan. Bake for 40–50 minutes, or until golden. The top may puff up slightly but will settle on standing.

Prep time 45 minutes
Cooking time 1 hour 20 minutes
Serves 8

nutrition per serve Energy 1175 kJ (281 Cal) Fat 5.1 g Saturated fat 1.9 g
Protein 31.1 g Carbohydrate 18.3 g Fibre 3.9 g Cholesterol 78 mg Sodium 366 mg

Italian fish rolls and sweet potato

1 large tomato

1 tbsp capers, drained and chopped

45 g (1½ oz/¼ cup) stuffed green
    olives in brine, drained and
    chopped

3 tbsp finely chopped lemon thyme

30 g (1 oz/¼ cup) finely grated
    romano cheese

2 tsp finely grated lemon zest

¼ tsp freshly ground black pepper

8 thin white skinless fish fillets
    (about 850 g/1 lb 14 oz)

250 ml (9 fl oz/1 cup) dry white wine

2 tbsp lemon juice

3 tbsp lemon thyme, extra

2 bay leaves

800 g (1 lb 12 oz) sweet potato,
    peeled and cut into 5 cm
    (2 in) pieces

1 Preheat the oven to 160°C (315°F/Gas 2–3). Peel and chop the tomato and score a cross in the base. Cover with boiling water for 30 seconds, then plunge into cold water. Drain and peel away the skin from the cross. Cut in half and scoop out the seeds. Roughly chop the flesh and mix with the capers, olives, lemon thyme, cheese, lemon zest and freshly ground pepper in a small bowl.

2 Put the fillets, skinned side up, on a flat surface. Spread the tomato mixture evenly onto each fillet, then roll up tightly and secure with a toothpick or skewer. Place in a single layer in a shallow casserole dish.

3 Pour the combined wine, juice, lemon thyme and bay leaves over the fish, cover with foil and bake for 20 minutes, or until the fish is cooked and flakes easily when tested with a fork.

4 Meanwhile, cook the sweet potato in a large saucepan of boiling water for 10 minutes or until cooked. Drain and roughly mash. Season with freshly ground black pepper. Serve with the fish rolls.

Prep time 30 minutes
Cooking time 30 minutes
Serves 4–6

Fettucine with seared tuna

400 g (14 oz) fettucine pasta

500 g (1 lb 2 oz) tuna steaks

olive oil spray

1 large red onion, cut into thin wedges

2 zucchini (courgettes), sliced into 7 cm (2¾ in) long thin strips

1 garlic clove, chopped

6 small gherkins, rinsed and chopped

1 large handful flat-leaf (Italian) parsley, chopped

zest and juice of 1 large lemon

mixed-leaf salad, to serve (optional)

Prep time 15 minutes
Cooking time 20 minutes
Serves 4

1 Cook the pasta in a large saucepan of boiling water for 10 minutes, or until al dente. Drain, reserving 250 ml (9 fl oz/1 cup) of the pasta water. Return the pasta to the saucepan.

2 Meanwhile, pat the fish dry with paper towels. Lightly spray a large, non-stick frying pan with the oil. Heat the oil, add the fish and cook for 2–3 minutes on each side, or until browned on the outside and still pink in the centre. Remove the fish from the pan. Set aside for a few minutes, then cut into 2 cm (¾ in) cubes.

3 Spray the frying pan with more oil and heat the pan. Add the onion, zucchini and garlic and cook for 2–3 minutes, or until softened. Stir in the gherkins, parsley, lemon zest and juice. Toss into the hot pasta together with the fish and enough of the reserved pasta water to moisten. Serve with a mixed-leaf salad.

nutrition per serve Energy **1307 kJ (312 Cal)** Fat **11.6 g** Saturated fat **4.3 g**
Protein **29.2 g** Carbohydrate **18.4 g** Fibre **9.3 g** Cholesterol **60 mg** Sodium **71 mg**

Lamb with cannellini bean purée

8 lean lamb cutlets

4 garlic cloves

1 tbsp chopped rosemary

2 tsp olive oil

2 x 400 g (14 oz) tins cannellini beans, drained

1 tsp ground cumin

125 ml (4 fl oz/½ cup) lemon juice

olive oil spray

2 tbsp balsamic vinegar

1 Trim the cutlets of excess fat from the outside edge and scrape the fat away from the bones. Put in a single layer in a shallow dish. Thinly slice 2 garlic cloves and mix with the rosemary, oil and some freshly ground black pepper. Pour over the meat, cover and refrigerate for 1 hour.

2 Rinse the beans and purée them in a food processor or blender with the remaining garlic, the cumin and half the lemon juice. Transfer to a pan, then set aside.

3 Lightly spray a non-stick frying pan with oil and cook the cutlets over medium heat for 1–2 minutes on each side. Add the vinegar and cook for 1 minute, turning to coat. Remove the cutlets and cover to keep warm. Add the remaining lemon juice to the pan and simmer for 2–3 minutes, or until the sauce thickens slightly. Warm the purée over medium heat and serve with the cutlets.

Prep time 30 minutes + 1 hour refrigeration
Cooking time 10 minutes
Serves 4

Grilled salmon with fennel salad

Fennel and orange salad

1 fennel bulb, with fronds

2 oranges, peeled and segmented

12 pitted black olives

1 tbsp snipped chives

1½ tbsp virgin olive oil

1 tbsp lemon juice

½ tsp dijon mustard

¼ tsp caster (superfine) sugar

500 g (1 lb 2 oz) piece salmon fillet

olive oil spray

**200 g (7 oz) baby English spinach
   leaves**

Prep time 20 minutes

Cooking time 2 minutes

Serves 4

1 To prepare the salad, trim the fronds from the fennel bulb and finely chop up enough fronds to fill a tablespoon. Remove the stalks from the fennel and cut a 5 mm (¼ in) thick slice off the base of the bulb. Cut the bulb in half, then finely slice and toss in a large bowl with the chopped fronds, orange segments, olives and chives. In a separate bowl, whisk the oil with the lemon juice, mustard and sugar. Season to taste with freshly ground black pepper, pour over the fennel mixture and toss gently to coat.

2 Heat the grill (broiler) to medium. Remove the bones and skin from the salmon and cut the flesh into 1 cm (½ in) thick slices. Lightly spray a grill tray with oil, put on the salmon slices, spray with more oil and season with freshly ground black pepper. Grill for 1–2 minutes, or until just cooked through.

3 Divide the spinach leaves among four large serving plates, top with the fennel and orange salad and arrange the salmon over the spinach. Serve warm.

Shish kebabs with risoni salad

200 g (7 oz/1 cup) risoni

2 tsp extra virgin olive oil

2 tsp balsamic vinegar

½ tsp grated lemon zest

2 tsp lemon juice

40 g (1¾ oz) baby rocket (arugula)
  leaves

1½ tbsp shredded basil

½ small red onion, finely sliced

Shish kebabs

250 g (9 oz) lean minced (ground)
  lamb

250 g (9 oz) minced (ground) veal

1 onion, finely chopped

2 garlic cloves, crushed

1 tsp ground allspice

1 tsp ground cinnamon

olive oil spray

1 First, make the risoni salad. Bring a saucepan of water to the boil, add the risoni and cook for about 12 minutes, or until tender. Drain, rinse under cold water, then drain again. Put the risoni in a large bowl with the oil, vinegar, lemon zest, lemon juice, rocket, basil and onion. Mix well, season to taste with freshly ground black pepper and refrigerate until ready to serve.

2 To make the shish kebabs, put the lamb, veal, onion, garlic, allspice and cinnamon in a food processor or blender with a little pepper. Process until fine, but not mushy. Divide the mixture into eight equal portions, then roll into long sausage-shaped shish kebabs. Insert a long metal skewer through the middle of each shish kebab, pressing the mixture firmly onto the skewers. Refrigerate for 30 minutes to firm.

3 Preheat a barbecue grill plate, flat plate or chargrill pan to medium. Spray the hotplate with oil and grill the kebabs for about 8–10 minutes, or until cooked through, turning often. Serve warm with the risoni salad.

Prep time 25 minutes +
30 minutes refrigeration time
Cooking time 20 minutes
Serves 4

nutrition per serve   Energy **1437 kJ (343 Cal)** Fat **9 g** Saturated fat **2.3 g**
Protein **18 g** Carbohydrate **45.3** Fibre **3.2 g** Cholesterol **96 mg** Sodium **348 mg**

Giant salmon balls

3 potatoes, cut into 5 cm (2 in) cubes

100 g (3½ oz/½ cup) long-grain rice

50 g (1¾ oz/½ cup) rolled (porridge) oats

415 g (14¾ oz) tin red salmon in spring water, drained and flaked

1 egg, lightly beaten

3 spring onions (scallions), chopped

2 tbsp lemon juice

2 tbsp sweet chilli sauce

80 g (2¾ oz/1 cup) fresh breadcrumbs

2 eggs, lightly beaten, extra

200 g (7 oz/2 cups) dry breadcrumbs

olive oil spray

lemon wedges, to serve

mixed-leaf salad, to serve

1 Boil, steam or microwave the potatoes until tender. Drain, mash and set aside to cool. Cook the rice in a saucepan of boiling water for 10 minutes, or until tender. Drain and cool.

2 Put the potato, rice, oats, salmon, egg, spring onions, lemon juice, chilli sauce and fresh breadcrumbs in a bowl, and mix together well. Season with freshly ground black pepper.

3 Divide the mixture into 8 portions and shape into balls. Dip in the egg, then in the dry breadcrumbs. Place on a baking tray lined with baking paper, cover and refrigerate for 30 minutes.

4 Preheat the oven to 200°C (400°F/Gas 6). Spray the salmon balls lightly with the oil and bake for 30 minutes, or until crisp, golden and heated through. Serve with lemon wedges and a large mixed-leaf salad.

Prep time 35 minutes +
30 minutes refrigeration
Cooking time 40 minutes
Makes 8 balls

nutrition per serve   Energy **1819 kJ (435 Cal)** Fat **9.8 g** Saturated fat **3.2 g**
Protein **41.3 g** Carbohydrate **41.7 g** Fibre **6.2 g** Cholesterol **85mg** Sodium **477 mg**

Steak sandwich with onion relish

Red onion relish

1 tsp olive oil

2 red onions, thinly sliced

2 tbsp soft brown sugar

2 tbsp balsamic vinegar

1 tbsp chopped thyme

250 g (9 oz) mixed mushrooms
   (flat, button, shiitake), sliced

olive oil spray

4 lean minute beef steaks, trimmed

3 large handfuls baby English
   spinach leaves

ciabatta or sourdough bread

mixed-leaf salad, to serve (optional)

Prep time 20 minutes
Cooking time 25 minutes
Serves 4

1   To make the red onion relish, heat the oil in a saucepan. Add the onion and cook over a low heat for 10 minutes, or until softened, taking care not to burn. Add the sugar and balsamic vinegar. Cook and stir often over a low heat for 10–12 minutes, or until softened and slightly syrupy. Stir in the thyme.

2   Meanwhile, put the mushrooms and 125 ml (4 fl oz/ ½ cup) water in a heavy-based frying pan. Bring to the boil, stirring to coat the mushrooms in the water. Simmer, covered, for 5 minutes, or until softened, making sure the mushrooms don't dry out. Stir once or twice. Remove lid and increase the heat to allow juice to evaporate. Season with freshly ground black pepper.

3   Lightly spray a chargrill pan or frying pan with the oil. Add the meat and cook for 1 minute on each side, or until cooked to your liking.

4   Very briefly microwave or steam the spinach until just wilted. Drain away any juices.

5   Slice the bread on the diagonal into 8 thick slices and toast. To serve, arrange 2 slices of bread on each plate. Top with the spinach, then the steak and mushrooms and finish with a dollop of the relish. Serve with a mixed-leaf salad.

Veal goulash

500 g (1 lb 2 oz) veal, cut into 2.5 cm
   (1 in) pieces

2 tbsp plain (all-purpose) flour

1 tbsp olive oil

olive oil spray

2 onions thinly sliced

2 garlic cloves, chopped

1 tbsp sweet Hungarian paprika

1 tsp ground cumin

440 g (15½ oz) tin reduced-salt
   diced tomatoes

2 carrots, sliced

½ red capsicum (pepper), chopped

½ green capsicum (pepper), chopped

250 ml (9 fl oz/1 cup) reduced-salt
   beef stock

125 ml (4 fl oz/½ cup) red wine

125 g (4 fl oz/½ cup) extra-light sour
   cream

chopped parsley, to garnish

1 Put the veal and flour in a plastic bag and shake to coat the veal. Shake off any excess flour. Heat the oil in a large deep heavy-based pan over medium heat. Brown the meat well in batches, then remove the meat and set aside.

2 Reheat the pan and spray with olive oil. Cook the onion, garlic, paprika and cumin for 5 minutes, stirring frequently. Return the meat and any juices to the pan with the tomato, carrot and capsicum. Cook and cover for 10 minutes.

3 Add the stock and wine and season with freshly ground black pepper. Stir well, then cover and simmer over very low heat for 1½ hours. Stir in half the sour cream, season with more pepper if needed and serve garnished with parsley and the remaining sour cream.

Prep time 25 minutes
Cooking time 2 hours
Serves 4

Reduced-fat moussaka

1 kg (2 lb 4 oz) eggplant (aubergine)

olive oil spray

2 onions, finely chopped

3 large garlic cloves, crushed

¼ tsp ground allspice

1 tsp ground cinnamon

500 g (1 lb 2 oz) lean minced
   (ground) lamb

2 tbsp no-added-salt tomato paste
   (concentrated purée)

125 ml (4 fl oz/½ cup) red wine

2 x 400 g (14 oz) tins reduced-salt
   tomatoes

3 tbsp chopped parsley

90 g (3¼ oz) low-fat cheddar cheese

20 g (¾ oz) olive or canola oil
   margarine

40 g (1½ oz/⅓ cup) plain flour

375 ml (13 fl oz/1½ cups) skim milk

150 g (5½ oz/⅔ cup) low-fat ricotta

pinch ground nutmeg

Prep time 30 minutes

Cooking time 1½ hours

Serves 6

1 Preheat the oven to 180°C (350°F/Gas 4). Cut the eggplant into 5 mm (¼ in) thick slices. Spray the eggplant with the oil and grill (broil) under a preheated grill (broiler) for 4 minutes on each side, or until golden.

2 Heat a large, non-stick saucepan and lightly spray with oil. Cook the onions for 3–4 minutes, or until softened. Add the garlic, allspice and cinnamon and cook for 1 minute. Add the lamb and cook for 3–4 minutes, or until cooked. Add the tomato paste, wine and tomatoes. Bring to the boil, then reduce the heat and simmer for 30–35 minutes, stirring occasionally, or until most of the liquid has evaporated. Stir in the parsley and season with freshly ground black pepper.

3 To make the white sauce, grate the cheese. Melt the margarine in a saucepan over a medium heat. Stir in the flour and cook for 1 minute. Remove from the heat and gradually stir in the milk. Return to the heat and stir constantly until the sauce boils and thickens. Reduce the heat and simmer for 2 minutes. Stir through ricotta and nutmeg until smooth and season with pepper.

4 Spoon half the meat sauce over the base of a 3 litre (105 fl oz/12 cup), 25 x 30 cm (10 x 12 in) ovenproof dish. Cover with half of the eggplant. Spoon over the remaining meat sauce and cover with the remaining eggplant. Spread over the sauce and sprinkle with the cheese. Bake for 30 minutes, or until golden. Stand for 5 minutes before serving.

Spicy chicken schnitzels

4 x 200 g (7 oz) chicken breast fillets

$^1/_2$ tbsp ground coriander

$^1/_2$ tbsp ground cumin

1/4 tsp chilli powder, or to taste

1 garlic clove, crushed

1 tbsp lemon juice

1 tbsp olive oil

250 g (9 oz/1 cup) low-fat plain yoghurt

$^1/_2$ tsp harissa paste, or to taste

$^1/_2$ tsp caster (superfine) sugar

2 tbsp finely chopped mint leaves, plus extra sprigs, to serve

nutrition per serve Energy **2160 kJ (516 Cal)** Fat **8.9 g** Saturated fat **2.1 g**
Protein **56.9 g** Carbohydrate **48.8 g** Fibre **3.7 g** Cholesterol **133 mg** Sodium **283 g**

Couscous salad

185 g (6½ oz/1 cup) couscous

300 g (10½ oz) tin chickpeas, rinsed and drained

75 g (2½ oz) cherry tomatoes, halved

½ small red onion, thinly sliced

Prep time 25 minutes +
15 minutes standing
Cooking time 10 minutes
Serves 4

1 Put the chicken breasts between two sheets of plastic wrap and flatten them with a mallet or rolling pin until 1½ cm (⅝ in) thick.

2 In a small bowl, mix the ground coriander, cumin, chilli powder, garlic, lemon juice and oil together to form a paste. Thoroughly rub the paste all over the chicken fillets, then cover and leave to stand for 10 minutes.

3 To make the couscous salad, pour 250 ml (9 fl oz/1 cup) boiling water over the couscous in a bowl. Cover with plastic wrap and leave for 5 minutes then fluff up with a fork. Stir through tomatoes and onion slices.

4 Heat the grill (broiler) to high. Put the chicken on a lightly oiled grill tray and grill for 6–8 minutes, or until cooked through, turning once.

5 Meanwhile, blend 1 tablespoon of the yoghurt in a bowl with the harissa and sugar. Stir in the remaining yoghurt and mint, season to taste with freshly ground black pepper.

6 Garnish the chicken with the extra mint sprigs and serve with the yoghurt mix and couscous.

nutrition per serve Energy **2056 kJ (491 Cal)** Fat **10.9 g** Saturated fat **3.6 g**
Protein **40.3 g** Carbohydrate **52.8 g** Fibre **7.8 g** Cholesterol **100 mg** Sodium **199 mg**

Stuffed beef fillet

1 tsp olive oil

2 French shallots, finely chopped

60 g (2¼ oz) mushrooms, finely
    chopped

20 g (¾ oz/½ cup) fresh wholemeal
    (whole-wheat) breadcrumbs

1 tbsp thyme

1 tbsp wholegrain mustard

olive oil spray

600 g (1 lb 5 oz) lean beef fillet

800 g (1 lb 12 oz) new potatoes, cut
    into bite-sized chunks

4 corn cobs, each cut in 4 pieces

Sauce

1 tsp orange zest

185 ml (6 fl oz/¾ cup) orange juice

1 tbsp orange marmalade

1 tbsp wholegrain mustard)

Prep time 30 minutes
Cooking time 55 minutes
Serves 4

1 Preheat the oven to 190°C (375°F/Gas 5). Heat the oil in a non-stick frying pan. Cook the shallots and mushrooms for 2 minutes, or until slightly softened. Put in a small bowl with the breadcrumbs and thyme leaves. Mix in the mustard and 2 teaspoons water to just moisten.

2 Cut along one side of the fillet to open out or create a butterfly. Spread the mushroom mixture over the surface. Enclose the filling and tie, at intervals, with string. Pat the meat dry with paper towels. Spray a heavy-based frying pan with oil. Heat and add the beef and cook on a high heat until browned all over. Put in a roasting tin. Roast for 25 minutes, or until cooked to your liking. Remove the meat from the oven, cover with foil and rest. Remove the string.

3 Meanwhile, line a baking tray with baking paper. Put the potatoes in a large saucepan of boiling water. Cook for 5 minutes, or until partially cooked. Drain well. Put the potatoes on the prepared tray. Season with freshly ground black pepper and spray with oil. Bake for 15–20 minutes, or until crisp and cooked through. Cook the corn cobs in a saucepan of boiling water for 8 minutes, or until tender. Drain.

4 Add the sauce ingredients to the roasting tin. Stir to dissolve the marmalade and allow it to reduce a little.

5 To serve, thickly slice the meat. Arrange the meat on plates, drizzle over a little of the sauce and serve with the potatoes and corn.

nutrition per serve   Energy **1132 kJ (271 Cal)** Fat **8.5 g** Saturated fat **2.9 g**
Protein **23.9 g** Carbohydrate **21.6 g** Fibre **5 g** Cholesterol **74 mg** Sodium **355 g**

Meatloaf

60 g (2¼ oz) sweet potato

1 carrot

canola or olive oil spray

2 onions, finely chopped

2 garlic cloves, crushed

125 g (4½ oz/1½ cups) fresh
    wholegrain breadcrumbs

2 tbsp chopped parsley

500 g (1 lb 2 oz) lean minced
    (ground) beef

2 tbsp worcestershire sauce

1 tsp dried basil

1 tbsp no-added-salt tomato paste
    (concentrated purée)

300 g (10½ oz) tin chickpeas,
    drained and rinsed

1 egg, lightly beaten

90 g (3¼ oz/1 cup) button
    mushrooms, thinly sliced

400 g (14 oz) tin reduced-salt
    tomatoes

1 tbsp dry white wine

1 tsp soft brown sugar

mixed-leaf salad, to serve

1 Preheat the oven to 200°C (400°F/Gas 6). Coarsely grate the sweet potato and carrot and set aside.

2 Heat a non-stick frying pan over medium heat, then spray with the oil. Add the onion and cook, stirring, for 2 minutes. Add 1 tablespoon water to prevent sticking, then add the garlic and stir for 3 minutes, or until the onion is golden brown. Set aside to cool completely.

3 Use your hands to thoroughly mix together the breadcrumbs, parsley, beef, Worcestershire sauce, basil, tomato paste, grated sweet potato and carrot and the cooled onion mixture. Mix in the chickpeas, egg and mushrooms. Season with freshly ground black pepper. Transfer to a 10 x 18 cm (4 x 7 in) non-stick loaf tin (or loaf tin lined with baking paper), pressing gently into the tin and smoothing the top.

4 To make the tomato sauce, push the undrained tomatoes through a sieve, then discard the contents of the sieve. Add the wine and sugar to the tomato mixture, then stir well. Spoon 3 tablespoons of the sauce over the meatloaf and bake for 15 minutes. Spoon another 3 tablespoons of sauce over the meatloaf, reduce the oven temperature to 190°C (375°F/Gas 5) and bake for 1 hour 10 minutes, basting occasionally with sauce. Slice and serve with any remaining sauce and a mixed-leaf salad.

Prep time 20 minutes

Cooking time 1 hour 20 minutes

Serves 6

Poached salmon kedgeree

2 eggs

750 ml (26 fl oz/3 cups) reduced-salt
   fish or chicken stock

125 ml (4 fl oz/$\frac{1}{2}$ cup) dry white
   wine

$\frac{1}{2}$ lemon, sliced

2 x 200 g (7 oz) salmon fillets

1 tsp canola oil margarine

1 large red onion, chopped

2 tbsp mild curry powder

2 tsp ground turmeric

300 g (10$\frac{1}{2}$ oz/1$\frac{1}{2}$ cups) basmati rice

60 g (2$\frac{1}{4}$ oz/$\frac{1}{2}$ cup) sultanas
   (golden raisins)

1 large handful flat-leaf (Italian)
   parsley, finely chopped

1 lemon, cut into 4 wedges, to serve
   (optional)

ready-made fruit chutney, to serve
   (optional)

mixed-leaf salad, to serve (optional)

Prep time 20 minutes
Cooking time 40 minutes
Serves 4

1   Put the eggs in a saucepan, cover with water and bring
to the boil. Boil for 5 minutes, drain and cool quickly in
cold water. Peel and chop roughly.

2   Heat a heavy-based frying pan that is 8 cm (3 in) deep
and 24 cm (9$\frac{1}{2}$ in) in diameter across the base. Add the
stock, wine and lemon slices and heat, then add the
fish. Lower the heat and simmer for 8 minutes, or until
just cooked through. Place the fish on a plate, remove
the skin and roughly flake with a fork. Strain the stock
into a jug to measure 750 ml (26 fl oz/3 cups). Set aside.
Wipe out the pan.

3   Heat the butter in the frying pan, add the onion and
cook for 2 minutes, or until softened. Add the curry
powder, the turmeric and rice. Stir to combine and cook
for 1 minute.

4   Stir in the reserved stock. Bring to the boil, lower the
heat, cover and simmer for 20 minutes, or until the rice
is cooked and the liquid has been absorbed.

5   Gently stir the chopped egg, fish, sultanas and half of
the parsley through the rice. Top with the remaining
parsley and lemon wedges on the side, if using. Serve
with a little fruit chutney and a mixed-leaf salad.

nutrition per serve   Energy **1495 kJ (357 Cal)** Fat **9.8 g** Saturated fat **4.1 g**
Protein **32.9 g** Carbohydrate **30.7 g** Fibre **5.6 g** Cholesterol **87 mg** Sodium **383 mg**

Shepherd's pie

1 kg (2 lb 4 oz) potatoes

6 large garlic cloves, peeled

4 tbsp skim milk

olive oil spray

1 large onion, finely chopped

3 large garlic cloves, crushed

2 celery sticks, finely chopped

2 carrots, diced

750 g (1 lb 10 oz) lean minced (ground) lamb

1½ tbsp plain (all-purpose) flour

2 tbsp no-added-salt tomato paste (concentrated purée)

2 tsp chopped thyme

2 tsp chopped rosemary

2 bay leaves

315 ml (10¾ fl oz/1¼ cups) reduced-salt beef stock

1 tbsp worcestershire sauce

mixed-leaf salad, to serve (optional)

Prep time 20 minutes

Cooking time 45 minutes

Serves 6

1 Preheat the oven to 180°C (350°F/Gas 4). Cut the potatoes into chunks and cook in a large saucepan of boiling water with the whole garlic cloves for 10–15 minutes, or until tender. Drain well and return to the saucepan. Mash the potato and garlic with a potato masher until smooth. Stir through the milk and season with freshly ground black pepper.

2 Heat a frying pan over medium heat, then spray with oil. Add the onion, crushed garlic, celery and carrot and cook for 5 minutes, or until the vegetables begin to soften (add water if needed). Remove from the pan.

3 Add the lamb and cook over a high heat until well browned, breaking up any lumps with the back of a spoon. Add the flour and cook for 1–2 minutes. Return the vegetables to the pan with the tomato paste, herbs, bay leaf, stock, sauce and nutmeg and bring to the boil. Reduce the heat and simmer for 5 minutes, or until thickened.

4 Pour the lamb mixture into a 2 litre (70 fl oz/4 cup) ovenproof dish. Spoon the potato over the top, smoothing the surface, then fluff with a fork. Bake for 25–30 minutes, or until lightly golden and crusty. Serve with a mixed-leaf salad.

Vegetarian

Vegetable and polenta pie

330 ml (11¼ fl oz/1⅓ cups) reduced-salt vegetable stock

150 g (5½ oz/1 cup) coarse polenta

50 g (1¾ oz/½ cup) finely grated parmesan cheese

1 tbsp olive oil

1 large onion, chopped

2 garlic cloves, crushed

2 eggplants (aubergines)

1 large red capsicum (pepper), diced

2 zucchini (courgettes), thickly sliced

150 g (5½ oz) button mushrooms, cut into quarters

400 g (14 oz) tin reduced-salt diced tomatoes

3 tsp balsamic vinegar

olive oil, for brushing

Prep time 25 minutes + refrigeration

Cooking time 50 minutes

Serves 6

1 Line a 22 cm (8½ in) round cake tin with foil. Pour the stock and 350 ml (12 fl oz) water into a saucepan and bring to the boil. Add the polenta in a thin stream and stir over low heat for 5 minutes, or until the liquid is absorbed and the mixture is thick and comes away from the side of the pan. Remove the pan from the heat and stir in the cheese until it melts all through the polenta. Spread into the tin, smoothing the surface as much as possible. Refrigerate until set.

2 Preheat the oven to 200°C (400°F/Gas 6). Heat the oil in a large saucepan and add the onion. Cook over medium heat, stirring occasionally, for 3 minutes, or until soft. Add the garlic and cook for 1 minute. Add the eggplant, capsicum, zucchini, mushrooms and tomatoes. Bring to the boil, then reduce the heat and simmer, covered, for 20 minutes, or until the vegetables are tender. Stir occasionally. Stir in the vinegar, then season with freshly ground black pepper.

3 Transfer the vegetable mixture to a 22 cm (8½ in) pie dish, piling it up slightly in the centre.

4 When the polenta has set, turn it out of the pan, peel off the foil and cut into 12 wedges. Arrange, smooth side down, in a single layer, over the vegetables—don't worry about any gaps. Brush lightly with olive oil and bake for 20 minutes, or until lightly brown and crisp.

nutrition per serve Energy **919 kJ (219 Cal)** Fat **1.8 g** Saturated fat **0.3 g**
Protein **6.7 g** Carbohydrate **40.8 g** Fibre **5.1 g** Cholesterol **0 mg** Sodium **271 mg**

Middle-Eastern potato casserole

¹/₄ **tsp saffron threads**

1 kg (2 lb 4 oz) potatoes, cut into large cubes

1 tsp olive oil

1 small onion, sliced

¹/₂ **tsp ground turmeric**

¹/₂ **tsp ground coriander**

250 ml (9 fl oz/1 cup) reduced-salt vegetable stock

1 garlic clove, crushed

30 g (1 oz/¹/₄ cup) raisins

1 tsp chopped flat-leaf (Italian) parsley

1 tsp chopped coriander (cilantro) leaves

1 Soak the saffron in 1 tablespoon of hot water. Put the potatoes in a saucepan of cold, salted water. Bring to the boil and cook until tender but still firm. Drain and set aside.

2 Heat the oil in a separate saucepan, add the onion, turmeric and ground coriander and cook over low heat for 5 minutes, or until the onion is soft.

3 Add the potato, vegetable stock and garlic. Bring to the boil, then reduce the heat and simmer for 10 minutes.

4 Add the saffron with its soaking water and the raisins, and cook for 10 minutes, or until the potato is soft and the sauce has reduced and thickened. Stir in the parsley and coriander.

Prep time 10 minutes

Cooking time 35 minutes

Serves 4

nutrition per serve Energy **1296 kJ (310 Cal)** Fat **13 g** Saturated fat **1.8 g**
Protein **11.2 g** Carbohydrate **34.2 g** Fibre **6.7 g** Cholesterol **0 mg** Sodium **113 mg**

Wild rice with pumpkin

190 g (6¾ oz/1 cup) wild rice, rinsed

300 g (10½ oz) jap or kent pumpkin, skin on, cut into 1 x 6 cm (½ x 2½ in) wedges

400 g (14 oz) tinned chickpeas, drained and rinsed

8 spring onions (scallions), finely sliced

50 g (1¾ oz/⅓ cup) currants

70 g (2½ oz/½ cup) pistachio nuts, roughly chopped

1 tsp garam masala

3 tbsp pepitas (pumpkin seeds)

1 tbsp olive oil

2 tsp finely grated orange zest

1 large handful coriander (cilantro) leaves

1 large handful mint, torn

1 Put the rice in a small saucepan over medium–high heat, add 625 ml (21½ fl oz/2½ cups) water and cover with a lid. Bring to the boil, then reduce the heat to low and simmer for 30–35 minutes, or until all liquid has been absorbed and the rice is cooked but still al dente.

2 Line a steamer with baking paper and punch with holes. Arrange pumpkin on top and cover with a lid. Sit steamer over a saucepan or wok of boiling water and steam for 5 minutes, or until pumpkin is tender when pierced with a sharp knife. Set aside to cool a little.

3 Put the chickpeas, spring onion, currants, pistachios, garam masala, pepitas, oil, orange zest, coriander and mint leaves in a large bowl and season with freshly ground black pepper. Add the steamed rice and pumpkin wedges and toss gently to combine. Arrange the salad in a bowl or on a platter and serve warm.

Prep time 20 minutes
Cooking time 40 minutes
Serves 4–6

Chickpea curry

220 g (7¾ oz/1 cup) dried chickpeas

2 tsp oil

2 onions, finely chopped

2 large tomatoes, chopped

½ tsp ground coriander

1 tsp ground cumin

1 tsp chilli powder

¼ tsp ground turmeric

1 tsp channa masala

1 small white onion, sliced, extra, to serve

mint and coriander (cilantro) leaves, to garnish

boiled rice, to serve (optional)

1 Put the chickpeas in a bowl, cover with water and leave to soak overnight. Drain, rinse, and put in a large saucepan. Cover with plenty of water and bring to the boil, then reduce the heat and simmer for 40 minutes, or until soft. Drain.

2 Heat the oil in a large saucepan, add the onion and cook over medium heat for 15 minutes, or until golden brown. Add the tomato, ground coriander and cumin, chilli powder, turmeric and channa masala, and 500 ml (16 fl oz/2 cups) water and cook for 10 minutes, or until the tomato is soft. Add the chickpeas, season with freshly ground pepper and cook for 7–10 minutes, or until the sauce thickens. Garnish with sliced onion and fresh mint and coriander leaves, and serve with rice.

Prep time 15 minutes + overnight soaking

Cooking time 1 hour 15 minutes

Serves 6

Harissa with couscous

Harissa

3 dried bird's eye chillies

3 large garlic cloves

1 tsp coriander seeds

½ tsp ground cumin

60 ml (2 fl oz/¼ cup) reduced-salt tomato passata (puréed tomatoes)

1 tbsp extra virgin olive oil

1 tbsp no-added-salt tomato paste (concentrated purée)

nutrition per serve
Energy **1589 kJ (380 Cal)** Fat **8.7 g** Saturated fat **1.1 g** Protein **14.5 g** Carbohydrate **57.4 g** Fibre **6.2 g** Cholesterol **2 mg** Sodium **195 mg**

2 tbsp roughly chopped coriander (cilantro) leaves

2 tbsp roughly chopped mint

250 g (9 oz/1 cup) Greek-style low-fat yoghurt

300 g (10½ oz/1⅔ cups) couscous

2 tsp olive oil

1 large onion, halved and thinly sliced

3 zucchini (courgettes), thinly sliced

2 large carrots, cut into fine matchsticks 2 cm (¾ in) long

400 g (14 oz) tin chickpeas, rinsed and drained

40 g (1½ oz/⅓ cup) sultanas (golden raisins)

30 g (1 oz/¼ cup) toasted slivered almonds

2 tbsp baby capers, rinsed and squeezed dry

1 To make the harissa, put the chillies, garlic, coriander seeds and cumin in a mini processor or blender. Blend for 30 seconds, or until roughly ground. Add the tomato passata, olive oil and tomato paste and blend for 12–15 seconds, or until smooth.

2 Put the coriander leaves, mint and yoghurt in a small bowl and mix to combine.

3 Prepare the couscous according to the manufacturer's instructions. Cover and set aside. Heat the oil in a large frying pan over medium heat. Add the onion and fry for 5–6 minutes, or until softened. Add the zucchini and carrot and fry for 5 minutes, or until just tender and beginning to brown. Stir in the chickpeas and sultanas. Add the couscous, stirring gently until well combined.

4 Divide the couscous mixture among serving plates and sprinkle with the toasted almonds and capers. Serve accompanied by the harissa and herbed yoghurt, to be added as desired.

Prep time 20 minutes
Cooking time 10 minutes
Serves 4–6

nutrition per serve   Energy **1310 kJ (313 Cal)** Fat **5.7** Saturated fat **0.7 g**
Protein **7.6 g** Carbohydrate **53.2 g** Fibre **5.1 g** Cholesterol **0 mg** Sodium **24 mg**

Curried eggplant stir-fry

1 tbsp vegetable oil

½–1 long green chilli, finely sliced

4 red Asian shallots, chopped

2 garlic cloves, finely sliced

2–3 tsp curry powder, to taste

350 g (12 oz) slender eggplants
(aubergines), cut on the diagonal
into 1 cm (½ in) slices

3 vine-ripened tomatoes, each cut
into 8 wedges

70 g (2½ oz/1½ cups) baby English
spinach leaves

boiled basmati rice, to serve

1 Heat the oil in a large wok and swirl to coat the sides. Add the green chilli, shallots and garlic and stir-fry over high heat for 1 minute. Stir in the curry powder and stir-fry for 1 minute.

2 Add the eggplant and stir-fry for 3 minutes, or until the eggplant has softened a little. Add the tomato and 125 ml (4 fl oz/½ cup) water. Cover the wok and cook for 10 minutes, or until the eggplant is cooked, stirring occasionally. Stir in the spinach leaves and cook for 1 minute, or until wilted. Serve immediately with boiled rice.

Prep time 15 minutes

Cooking time 15 minutes

Serves 4

Moroccan vegetable tagine

2 tsp oil

2 onions, chopped

1 tsp ground ginger

2 tsp ground paprika

2 tsp ground cumin

1 cinnamon stick

pinch of saffron threads

nutrition per serve
Energy **1929 kJ (461 Cal)** Fat **7.7 g** Saturated fat **0.8 g** Protein **14.3 g** Carbohydrate **78.4 g** Fibre **10.6 g** Cholesterol **0 mg** Sodium **283 mg**

1.5 kg (3 lb 5 oz) mixed vegetables, peeled, and cut into large chunks (carrot, eggplant (aubergine), orange sweet potato, parsnip, potato, pumpkin (winter squash))

½ preserved lemon, rinsed, pith and flesh removed, thinly sliced

400 g (14 oz) tin reduced-salt peeled tomatoes

250 ml (9 fl oz/1 cup) reduced-salt vegetable stock

100 g (3½ oz) dried pears, halved

60 g (2¼ oz) pitted prunes

2 zucchini (courgettes), cut into large chunks

300 g (10½ oz) instant couscous

1 tbsp olive oil

3 tbsp chopped flat-leaf (Italian) parsley

50 g (1¾ oz/⅓ cup) almonds

1 Preheat the oven to 180°C (350°F/Gas 4). Heat the oil in a large saucepan or ovenproof dish, add the onion and cook over medium heat for 5 minutes, or until soft. Add the spices and cook for 3 minutes.

2 Add the vegetables and cook, stirring, until coated with the spices and the outsides begin to soften. Add the lemon, tomatoes, stock, pears and prunes. Cover, transfer to the oven and cook for 30 minutes. Add the zucchini and cook for 15–20 minutes, or until the vegetables are tender.

3 Cover the couscous with the olive oil and 500 ml (17 fl oz/2 cups) boiling water, cover and leave until all the water has been absorbed. Fluff with a fork.

4 Remove the cinnamon stick from the vegetables, then stir in the parsley. Serve on a large platter with the couscous formed in a ring and the vegetable tagine in the centre, sprinkle with almonds.

Prep time 25 minutes
Cooking time 1 hour
Serves 4–6

nutrition per serve Energy **1608 kJ (384 Cal)** Fat **6.5 g** Saturated fat **1.3 g**
Protein **10.8 g** Carbohydrate **66 g** Fibre **5 g** Cholesterol **1 mg** Sodium **37 mg**

Pumpkin bhaji

1 tbsp vegetable oil

1 tsp yellow mustard seeds

1 onion, finely chopped

1 tsp grated fresh ginger

1 green chilli, seeded and chopped

1 tsp ground coriander

½ tsp garam masala

½ tsp ground turmeric

½ tsp ground cumin

½ tsp chilli flakes

750 g (1 lb 10 oz) pumpkin (winter
   squash), peeled, seeded and cut
   into 3 cm (1¼ in) cubes

400 g (14 oz) tin reduced-salt diced
   tomatoes

1 tsp soft brown sugar

3 tbsp low-fat plain yoghurt

coriander (cilantro) leaves, to serve

boiled basmati rice, to serve

Prep time 20 minutes
Cooking time 35 minutes
Serves 4

1 Heat the oil in a large wok and cook the mustard seeds until they just start to pop. Add the onion, ginger and chilli and stir-fry for 2 minutes. Add the coriander, garam masala, turmeric, cumin and chilli flakes and stir-fry for 1 minute, or until aromatic.

2 Stir in the pumpkin, chopped tomatoes, sugar and 125 ml (4 fl oz/½ cup) water. Bring to the boil, then reduce the heat and simmer, covered, for 30 minutes, or until the pumpkin is tender. Stir occasionally. Gently fold in the yoghurt and scatter with coriander leaves before serving with boiled rice.

Chilli tofu stir-fry

1 tbsp canola oil

1 tsp bottled crushed chilli

2 tsp grated fresh ginger

2 garlic cloves, crushed

250 g (9 oz) firm tofu, cut into 1.5 cm
($\frac{5}{8}$ in) cubes

8 spring onions (scallions), sliced on
the diagonal

150 g (5½ oz) fresh baby corn, halved
lengthways

150 g (5½ oz) snowpeas
(mangetout), topped and tailed

500 g (1 lb 2 oz) hokkien (egg)
noodles

40 g (1½ oz/¼ cup) cashew nuts

1 tbsp reduced-salt soy sauce

125 ml (4 fl oz/½ cup) reduced-salt
vegetable stock

1 handful coriander (cilantro) leaves

1 Heat the oil in a wok over medium heat and swirl to
coat the sides. Add the chilli, ginger and garlic and stir-
fry for about 2–3 minutes, or until aromatic. Add the
tofu cubes, spring onion and baby corn and stir-fry for
2–3 minutes.

2 Add the snowpeas, noodles and cashews and cook,
stirring, for 3–5 minutes, or until the vegetables are
almost tender. Stir in the soy sauce and stock, then
bring to the boil and simmer for 2 minutes, or until
slightly reduced. Stir in the coriander and
serve immediately.

Prep time 15 minutes

Cooking time 15 minutes

Serves 4

nutrition per serve
Energy **934 kJ (223 Cal)** Fat **19.8 g** Saturated fat **4.3 g**
Protein **4.1 g** Carbohydrate **5.2 g** Fibre **5.1 g** Cholesterol **0 mg** Sodium **265 mg**

Asian greens with chilli marinade

Marinade

15 g (½ oz/¼ cup) shredded coconut

2 garlic cloves, roughly chopped

2 cm (¾ in) piece ginger, roughly chopped

1 red Asian shallot, roughly chopped

1 small red chilli, sliced

2 tbsp canola oil

1 tbsp rice vinegar

2 tsp fish sauce

1 tsp soft brown sugar

2 spring onions (scallions), sliced

1.1 kg (2 lb 7 oz/2 bunches) Asian green vegetables

boiled rice, to serve (optional)

Prep time 25 minutes + 1 hour marinating

Cooking time 10 minutes

Serves 4

1 To make the marinade, heat a dry frying pan over medium heat. Add the shredded coconut and fry, stirring, for 3–4 minutes, or until brown. Transfer the coconut to a spice mill or mini processor, add the garlic, ginger, shallot and chilli and blend until finely chopped. Add 1 tablespoon of oil, vinegar, fish sauce and sugar and blend in short bursts until blended. Transfer to a large bowl and stir in the spring onion.

2 Slice the Asian green vegetables into 8 cm (3¼ in) lengths and divide these into stems and leaves. Heat a wok or large frying pan over medium–high heat and add the remaining oil. Add the vegetable stems and stir-fry for 1 minute. Add the vegetable leaves and stir-fry for 45–60 seconds, or until they wilt and turn bright green.

3 Transfer the hot vegetables to the bowl with the marinade and toss to coat. Marinate for at least 1 hour to allow the flavours to develop.

nutrition per serve   Energy 1610 kJ (385 Cal) Fat 5.4 g Saturated fat 1.8 g
Protein 12.6 g Carbohydrate 65.5 g Fibre 6.8 g Cholesterol 11 mg Sodium 31 mg

Creamy ratatouille with farfalle

350 g (12 oz) baby eggplants
　　(aubergines)

olive oil spray

1 large red capsicum (pepper)

1 large green capsicum (pepper)

2 tsp olive oil

1 onion, diced

4 garlic cloves, crushed

400 g (14 oz) tin reduced-salt diced
　　tomatoes

2 zucchini (courgettes), finely diced

1 tbsp chopped thyme

3 tbsp chopped parsley

3 tbsp red wine

2 tsp soft brown sugar

2 tsp no-added-salt tomato paste
　　(concentrated purée)

2½ handfuls basil, plus extra whole
　　leaves, to serve

500 g (1 lb 2 oz) farfalle pasta

100 ml (3½ fl oz) extra-light pouring
　　(whipping) cream

Prep time 30 minutes
Cooking time 55 minutes
Serves 6

1　Heat the grill (broiler) to high. Cut the ends off
the eggplants and slice the flesh length-ways into
2 cm (¾ in) strips. Spread the eggplant on a baking tray
lined with foil and lightly spray with spray oil. Grill for
about 3–5 minutes, or until golden brown, then remove.

2　Cut the capsicums into large flat pieces and remove the
seeds and membranes. Cook, skin side up, under the
hot grill until the skin blackens and blisters. Leave to
cool in a plastic bag, then peel away the skin and cut
the flesh into strips.

3　Heat the oil in a large frying pan. Add the onion and
garlic and gently sauté for 3 minutes. Stir through the
grilled eggplant, capsicum, tomato, zucchini, thyme,
parsley, wine, sugar, tomato paste and basil. Season well
with freshly ground pepper, then simmer, uncovered, for
30 minutes, stirring occasionally.

4　While the ratatouille is simmering, cook the pasta in
a large saucepan of rapidly boiling salted water for
10 minutes, or until al dente. Drain well and
keep warm.

5　Take the ratatouille off the heat, add the cream and stir
through gently. Divide the pasta among six serving
bowls and spoon the ratatouille over the top. Garnish
with the extra basil leaves and serve.

Pasta siracusa

2 tsp olive oil

2 garlic cloves, crushed

1 large green capsicum (pepper), thinly sliced

2 x 400 g (14 oz) tins reduced-salt diced tomatoes

2 zucchini (courgettes), chopped

2 anchovy fillets in brine, drained and chopped

1 tbsp capers, chopped

3 tbsp black olives in brine, rinsed, pitted and halved

2 tbsp chopped basil

500 g (1 lb 2 oz) spaghetti or linguine

65 g (1¼ oz/⅓ oz/⅔ cup) grated parmesan cheese, to serve

1 Heat the oil in a large, deep frying pan and cook garlic for 30 seconds over low heat. Add the capsicum, tomatoes, zucchini, anchovies, capers, olives and 125 ml (4 fl oz/½ cup) water. Cook for 20 minutes, stirring occasionally.

2 Add the basil to the pan and stir well. Season to taste with freshly ground black pepper.

3 Meanwhile, cook pasta in a large saucepan of boiling water for 10 minutes, or until al dente. Drain well. Serve pasta topped with the sauce and grated parmesan.

Prep time 20 minutes

Cooking time 30 minutes

Serves 4–6

Spinach shells in tomato sauce

30 (220 g/7 oz) large pasta shells

250 g (9 oz) frozen leaf spinach, defrosted

500 g (1 lb 2 oz/2 cups) low-fat, reduced-salt cottage cheese

250 g (9 oz/1 cup) low-fat ricotta cheese

2 spring onions (scallions), finely chopped

1 tsp nutmeg

500 ml (17 fl oz/2 cups) reduced-salt tomato passata (puréed tomatoes)

250 ml (9 fl oz/1 cup) reduced-salt vegetable stock or water

60 g (2¼ oz/½ cup) grated reduced-fat cheddar cheese (we used 50% reduced-fat)

1 Cook the pasta in a large saucepan of boiling salted water for 10 minutes, or until al dente. Drain and cool under cold water.

2 Using clean hands, squeeze the excess moisture from the spinach. Put in a large bowl, add the cottage and ricotta cheeses, spring onions and nutmeg. Season well with freshly ground black pepper. Combine well using a fork.

3 Preheat the oven to 180°C (350°F/Gas 4). Combine half the tomato passata and half the stock or water and pour over the base of a 32 x 25 x 5 cm (12½ x 10 x 2 in) ovenproof dish. Spoon the spinach mixture into the pasta shells and put them in a single layer over the sauce. Spread over the remaining passata and stock or water and sprinkle over the cheese mixture.

4 Bake for 45 minutes, or until the pasta is cooked. Serve hot with a mixed green salad.

Prep time 20 minutes

Cooking time 55 minutes

Serves 4–6

nutrition per serve
Energy **1667 kJ (398 Cal)** Fat **7.9 g** Saturated fat **2.9 g**
Protein **23.7 g** Carbohydrate **55.4 g** Fibre **6.9 g** Cholesterol **10 mg** Sodium **232 mg**

Red lentil and ricotta lasagne

90 g (3¼ oz/½ cup) red lentils

2 tsp olive oil

2–3 garlic cloves, crushed

1 large onion, chopped

1 small red capsicum (pepper), chopped

2 zucchini (courgettes), sliced

1 celery stalk, sliced

2 x 400 g (14 oz) tins reduced-salt diced tomatoes

2 tbsp no-added-salt tomato paste (concentrated purée)

1 tsp dried oregano

40 g (1½ oz/⅓ cup) cornflour (cornstarch)

750 ml (26 fl oz/3 cups) skim milk

¼ onion

½ tsp ground nutmeg

350 g (12 oz/1⅓ cups) low-fat ricotta cheese

12 dried or fresh lasagne sheets

60 g (2¼ oz/½ cup) grated reduced-fat cheddar cheese

Prep time 30 minutes +
30 minutes soaking

Cooking time 1 hour 50 minutes

Serves 6

1 Pour lentils in a large bowl, cover with boiling water and soak for 30 minutes. Drain. Heat oil in a large saucepan, add garlic and onion and cook for 2 minutes. Add the capsicum, zucchini and celery and cook for 2–3 minutes, or until softened. Add lentils, tomatoes, tomato paste, oregano and 375 ml (13 fl oz/1½ cups) water. Bring slowly to the boil, then reduce the heat and simmer for 30 minutes, or until the lentils are tender. Stir occasionally. Preheat oven to 180°C (350°F/Gas 4).

2 To make the white sauce, blend the cornflour with 2 tablespoons of the milk in a saucepan until smooth. Pour the remaining milk into the pan, add the onion and stir over low heat until the mixture boils and thickens. Add the nutmeg and season with freshly ground black pepper, then cook over low heat for 5 minutes. Remove the onion.

3 Beat the ricotta with about 125 ml (4 fl oz/½ cup) of the white sauce. Spread one-third of the lentil mixture over the base of a 3-litre (105 fl oz/12 cup) ovenproof dish. Cover with a layer of lasagne sheets. Spread another third of the lentil mixture over the pasta, then spread the ricotta mixture evenly over the top. Follow with another layer of lasagne, then the remaining lentils. Pour the white sauce over the top. Sprinkle with the grated cheese. Bake for 1 hour, covering with lightly oiled foil if the top starts to brown too much. Stand for 5 minutes before cutting. Serve with a salad.

Vegetable stew with dal

Dal

165 g (5½ oz/¾ cup) yellow split
   peas

5 cm (2 in) piece of ginger, grated

2–3 garlic cloves, crushed

1 red chilli, seeded and chopped

3 tomatoes

1 tbsp oil

1 tsp yellow mustard seeds

1 tsp cumin seeds

1 tsp ground cumin

1/2 tsp garam masala

1 red onion, cut into thin wedges

nutrition per serve
Energy **746 kJ (178 Cal)** Fat **4.5 g** Saturated fat **0.4 g**
Protein **10 g** Carbohydrate **21.2 g** Fibre **7.3 g** Cholesterol **0 mg** Sodium **282 mg**

3 slender eggplants (aubergines),
    thickly sliced

2 carrots, thickly sliced

¼ cauliflower, cut into florets

375 ml (12 fl oz/1½ cups) reduced-
    salt vegetable stock

2 small zucchini (courgettes), thickly
    sliced

90 g (3 oz/½ cup) frozen peas

15 g (½ oz/½ cup) fresh coriander
    (cilantro) leaves

Prep time 25 minutes + 2 hours
soaking
Cooking time 1 hour 35 minutes
Serves 4–6

1 To make the dal, put the split peas in a bowl, cover with water and soak for 2 hours. Drain. Place in a large saucepan with the ginger, garlic, chilli and 750 ml (26 fl oz/3 cups) water. Bring to the boil, reduce the heat and simmer for 45 minutes, or until soft.

2 Score a cross in the base of each tomato, soak in boiling water for 30 seconds, then plunge into cold water and peel skin away from cross. Seed and thoroughly chop.

3 Heat the oil in a large saucepan. Cook the spices over medium heat for 30 seconds, or until fragrant. Add the onion and cook for 2 minutes, or until the onion is soft. Stir in the tomato, eggplant, carrot and cauliflower.

4 Add the dal and stock, mix together well and simmer, covered, for 45 minutes, or until the vegetables are tender. Stir occasionally. Add the zucchini and peas during the last 10 minutes of cooking. Stir in the coriander leaves and serve.

nutrition per serve   Energy **640 kJ (153 Cal)** Fat **1.9 g** Saturated fat **0.4 g**
Protein **5.4 g** Carbohydrate **24.8 g** Fibre **6 g** Cholesterol **0mg** Sodium **47 mg**

Baked vegetables with rosemary

2 carrots

2 parsnips

2 large potatoes

300 g (10½ oz) pumpkin (winter squash)

olive oil spray

2 finger eggplants (aubergines)

4 large garlic cloves, unpeeled

4 small sprigs of rosemary

2 tbsp chopped parsley

Prep time 15 minutes

Cooking time 40 minutes

Serves 4

1 Preheat the oven to 200°C (400°F/Gas 6). Wash the vegetables and pat dry. Cut the carrots and parsnips in half lengthways, then crossways. Quarter the potatoes. Cut the unpeeled pumpkin into chunks.

2 Put the carrot, parsnip, potato and pumpkin in a baking dish and spray lightly with oil. Sprinkle with freshly ground black pepper. Bake for 20 minutes, turning occasionally.

3 Meanwhile, cut the eggplants in half lengthways and make thin shallow cuts through the skin. Add to the baking dish with the garlic and rosemary sprigs. Spray with more oil and cook, turning occasionally, for 20 minutes, or until all of the vegetables are tender. To serve, squeeze out the soft garlic and serve with the vegetables and the rosemary. Sprinkle with the parsley and more freshly ground black pepper.

nutrition per serve   Energy **693 kJ (166 Cal)** Fat **4.2** Saturated fat **0.6 g**
Protein **11.8 g** Carbohydrate **16.9 g** Fibre **8.2 g** Cholesterol **0 mg** Sodium **25 mg**

Caramelised onions with lentils

225 g (8 oz/1¼ cups) puy lentils or tiny blue-green lentils

1 tbsp olive oil

2 red onions, finely sliced

2 garlic cloves, finely chopped

1 tsp ground coriander

1 tsp ground cumin

550 g (1 lb 4 oz) English spinach, rinsed well
   and stems trimmed

1 tbsp lemon juice

2 tbsp chopped coriander (cilantro) leaves

1 Put the lentils in a small saucepan over high heat and
add 625 ml (21½ fl oz/2½ cups) water. Bring to the boil,
then cover with a fitted lid, reduce the heat to very low
and simmer the lentils for 35 minutes, or until all of the
water has been absorbed and the lentils are tender.

2 Meanwhile, heat the oil in a frying pan over medium
heat and cook the onion, stirring occasionally, for
20 minutes, or until soft and caramelised. Add the
garlic, ground coriander and cumin, season with freshly
ground black pepper and cook for a further 3 minutes.
Remove from the heat.

Prep time 20 minutes
Cooking time 1 hour
Serves 6

3 Put the spinach in a large steamer and cover with a lid.
Sit the steamer over a saucepan or wok of boiling water
and steam for 3–5 minutes, or until wilted. Combine
the lentils, onion mixture and spinach in a large bowl,
add the lemon juice and coriander leaves and toss well.
Serve immediately.

nutrition per serve

Energy **1233 kJ (295 Cal)** Fat **7.1 g** Saturated fat **2 g**
Protein **33.2 g** Carbohydrate **20.2 g** Fibre **7.9 g** Cholesterol **79 mg** Sodium **416 mg**

Spinach pie

olive or canola oil spray

1.5 kg (3 lb 5 oz) English spinach, trimmed and washed

2 tsp olive oil

1 onion, chopped

4 spring onions, chopped

750 g (1 lb 10 oz) low-fat cottage cheese

2 eggs, lightly beaten

2 garlic cloves, crushed

pinch of ground nutmeg

15 g (½ oz/¼ cup) chopped mint

8 sheets filo pastry

40 g (1½ oz/½ cup) fresh breadcrumbs

Prep time 25 minutes
Cooking time 50 minutes
Serves 6

1 Preheat the oven to 180°C (350°F/Gas 4). Lightly spray a 24 cm square x 5 cm deep (1.5 litre/52 fl oz/6 cups) ovenproof dish with oil. Place the spinach in a large pan. Cover and cook for 2–3 minutes, or until just wilted. Drain, cool, then squeeze dry and chop.

2 Heat the oil in a small frying pan. Cook the onion and spring onion for 2–3 minutes, or until softened. Combine with the spinach. Stir in the cheese, egg, garlic, nutmeg and mint. Season with freshly ground black pepper, and mix thoroughly.

3 Spray a sheet of filo pastry with spray oil. Fold in half widthways and line the base and sides of the dish. Repeat with three more sheets. Keep the unused sheets moist by covering with a damp tea towel (dish towel).

4 Sprinkle the breadcrumbs over the pastry. Spread the filling in the dish. Fold over any overlapping pastry. Spray and fold another sheet and place on top. Repeat with three more sheets. Tuck the pastry in. Spray the top with more oil. Score squares on top. Bake for 40 minutes, or until golden.

Chickpea burgers

Chickpea patties

2 tsp olive oil

1 small onion, finely chopped

2 garlic cloves, crushed

800 g (28 oz) tinned chickpeas, drained and rinsed

95 g ($3\frac{1}{2}$ oz/$\frac{1}{2}$ cup) cooked brown rice

50 g ($1\frac{3}{4}$ oz/$\frac{1}{3}$ cup) sun-dried tomatoes, chopped

nutrition per serve   Energy **1530 kJ (365 Cal)** Fat **6.1 g** Saturated fat **1.2 g**
Protein **15.3 g** Carbohydrate **56.6 g** Fibre **9.2 g** Cholesterol **3 mg** Sodium **395 mg**

1 eggplant (aubergine), cut into
    1 cm (½ in) slices

1 large red onion, sliced into rings

spray olive oil

2 large handfuls rocket (arugula)
    leaves

6 pieces Turkish bread

Spicy yoghurt dressing

200 g (7 oz) reduced-fat plain
    yoghurt

1 garlic clove, crushed

¼ tsp ground cumin

¼ tsp ground coriander

Prep time 30 minutes + 1 hour
refrigeration

Cooking time 20 minutes

makes 6

1 To make the chickpea patties, heat the oil in a frying
pan and cook the onion over medium heat for
2 minutes, or until soft and lightly golden. Add garlic
and cook for 1 more minute, then remove from heat
and allow to cool slightly. Put onion mixture in a food
processor with chickpeas, rice and sun-dried tomato.
Using a pulse action, process in short bursts until
mixture is combined and chickpeas are broken up,
scraping the bowl down with a spatula a few times
during processing. Season with black pepper, then
shape mixture into six patties about 8 cm (3¼ in) in
diameter. Place on a tray lined with plastic wrap, then
cover and refrigerate for 1 hour.

2 Put all the spicy yoghurt dressing ingredients in a small
bowl and mix together well. Refrigerate until needed.

3 Preheat a barbecue hot plate to moderately hot. Spray
eggplant slices and onion rings lightly on each side with
spray oil. Cook eggplant and onion on hotplate until
tender and lightly golden—the eggplant will need about
3–4 minutes each side, the onion about 5 minutes.
Transfer vegetables to a plate and set aside.

4 Spray one side of the chickpea patties lightly with oil,
then put them face-down on the hotplate and cook for
3 minutes. Spray the other side of patties with a little
more oil, then turn and cook for a further 3 minutes.

5 While chickpea patties are cooking, arrange rocket,
barbecued eggplant and onion on Turkish bread slices.
Add the hot chickpea patties, dollop with some spicy
yoghurt dressing and serve at once.

Sweet potato strudel

250 g (9 oz) orange sweet potato, cut into 2 cm (¾ in) cubes

3 garlic cloves, unpeeled

olive oil spray

250 g (9 oz) English spinach, blanched and excess moisture squeezed out, roughly chopped

40 g (1½ oz/¼ cup) pine nuts, toasted

125 g (4½ oz) low-fat feta cheese, crumbled

3 spring onions (scallions), including green part, chopped

50 g (1 ¾ oz) black olives, pitted and sliced

15 g (½ oz/¼ cup) chopped basil

1 tbsp chopped rosemary

8 sheets filo pastry

1 tbsp sesame seeds

Prep time 25 minutes
Cooking time 1 hour 5 minutes
Serves 6

1 Preheat the oven to moderate 180°C (350°F/Gas 4). Put the sweet potato and garlic in a roasting tin and spray with oil. Roast for 30 minutes, or until the sweet potato is soft. Remove the garlic when it is soft, after about 15 minutes. Cool slightly.

2 Combine the sweet potato, spinach, pine nuts, feta, spring onion, olives, basil and rosemary. Peel the garlic cloves and roughly chop the flesh, then add to the sweet potato mixture, and season with freshly ground black pepper.

3 Cover the pastry with a damp tea towel (dish towel) to prevent it drying out. Lay the pastry out in front of you, in a stack, and spray each layer with oil. Spread the filling in the centre of the pastry, covering an area 10 x 30 cm. Fold in the shorter ends of the pastry. Fold the long side closest to you over the filling, then carefully roll up. Place the strudel on a greased baking tray, seam side down. Spray with oil and sprinkle with sesame seeds. Bake for 35 minutes, or until crisp and golden. Serve warm.

Silverbeet parcels

**500 ml (17 fl oz/2 cups) reduced-salt
vegetable stock**

2 tsp olive oil

1 onion, chopped

2 garlic cloves, crushed

110 g (3¾ oz/½ cup) arborio rice

1 red capsicum (pepper), chopped

250 g (9 oz) mushrooms, chopped

**60 g (2¼ oz/½ cup) reduced-fat
cheddar cheese, grated**

**15 g (½ oz/¼ cup) shredded fresh
basil**

6 large silverbeet leaves

**2 x 400 g (14 oz) tins reduced-salt
diced tomatoes**

1 tbsp balsamic vinegar

1 tsp soft brown sugar

Prep time 40 minutes

Cooking time 1 hour

Serves 6

1 Heat the stock in a pan and maintain at simmering
point. Heat the oil in a large pan, add the onion and
garlic and cook until softened. Add the rice, capsicum
and mushrooms, and stir until well combined.
Gradually add 125 ml (4 fl oz/1/2 cup) hot stock,
stirring until the liquid is absorbed. Add the stock, a
little at a time, stirring until it is all absorbed and the
rice is tender (about 20 minutes). Remove from the
heat, add the cheese and basil, and season well with
freshly ground black pepper.

2 Meanwhile, trim the stalks from the silverbeet and cook
the leaves, a few at a time, in a large pan of boiling
water for 30 seconds, or until wilted. Drain on a tea
towel (dish towel). Cut away any tough white veins
from the leaves. Put a portion of risotto filling in the
centre of each leaf, fold in the sides and roll up carefully.
Tie with string.

3 Put the tomato, vinegar and sugar in a large, deep non-
stick frying pan and stir to combine. Add the silverbeet
parcels, cover and simmer for 10 minutes. Remove the
string and serve with tomato sauce.

Vegetable frittata

250 g (9 oz) pumpkin (winter squash), cubed

300 g (10½ oz) potato, cubed

100 g (3½ oz) broccoli florets

2 tsp olive oil

1 small onion, chopped

1 small red capsicum (pepper), chopped

2 tbsp finely chopped fresh parsley

olive oil spray

3 eggs

2 egg whites

mixed-leaf salad, to serve

1 Steam the zucchini, pumpkin, potato and broccoli until tender, then transfer to a bowl.

2 Heat the oil in a non-stick frying pan, about 22 cm (8½ in) in diameter. Add the onion and capsicum, and cook for 3 minutes, or until tender. Transfer to the bowl of steamed vegetables, along with the chopped parsley.

3 Heat a frying pan over medium heat and spray with oil. Return all vegetables to pan and spread out with a spatula to an even thickness. Beat eggs and egg whites together and pour into pan, tilting to distribute evenly.

4 Cook over medium heat until egg is almost set, but still runny on top. Wrap handle of the pan in a damp tea towel (dish towel) to protect it and place pan under grill to cook frittata top (pierce gently with a fork to make sure it is cooked through). Cut into wedges and serve.

Prep time 25 minutes

Cooking time 25 minutes

Serves 6

Sweet things

Mango passionfruit sorbet

230 g (8½ oz/1 cup) caster
  (superfine) sugar

90 g (3¼ oz/⅓ cup) passionfruit
  pulp (about 8 passionfruit)

½ large mango, chopped

1 large peach, chopped

2 tbsp lemon juice

1 egg white

Prep time 20 minutes +
refrigeration time + 8 hours
freezing
Cooking time 5 minutes
Serves 6

1 Put the sugar in a saucepan with 250 ml (9 fl oz/1 cup)
water. Stir over low heat until the sugar has dissolved.
Increase the heat, bring to the boil and boil for
1 minute. Transfer to a glass bowl, cool, then refrigerate.
Strain the passionfruit pulp, reserving 1 tablespoon of
the seeds.

2 Blend the fruit, passionfruit juice and lemon juice in a
blender until smooth. With the motor running, add the
cold sugar syrup and 150 ml (5 fl oz) water. Stir in the
passionfruit seeds. Freeze in a shallow container,
stirring occasionally, for about 5 hours, or until
almost set.

3 Break up the icy mixture roughly with a fork or spoon,
transfer to a bowl and beat with electric beaters until
smooth and fluffy. Beat the egg white in a small bowl
until firm peaks form, then fold into the mixture until
just combined. Spread into a loaf tin and return to the
freezer until firm. Transfer to the refrigerator, to soften,
15 minutes before serving.

nutrition per serve Energy **546 kJ (130 Cal)** Fat **0.2 g** Saturated fat **0 g**
Protein **0.6 g** Carbohydrate **30.8 g** Fibre **3.7 g** Cholesterol **0 mg** Sodium **7 mg**

Pear sorbet

**6 large (2 kg/4 lb 8 oz) very ripe
  pears**
25 g (1 oz/1 cup) sucralose

Prep time 40 minutes + overnight
freezing
Cooking time 15 minutes
Serves 4–6

1 Thickly peel the pears, then core them and slice them
into thick pieces. Place the pears in a large saucepan,
just cover with water and simmer for about 10 minutes,
or until tender. Drain and allow to cool.

2 Purée pears in a blender or food processor until smooth.

3 Combine the sucralose and 200 ml (7 fl oz) water in a
saucepan over medium heat. Allow the syrup to cool.
Mix together the sucralose syrup and pear purée, then
pour into a shallow metal pan. Freeze until just solid.

4 Remove the pan from the freezer. Beat or process until
a 'slush' forms. Return to the pan and freeze until firm.
Remove from freezer 15–20 minutes before serving.

Mixed berry sundae

45 g (1¾ oz) sucralose

juice of 1 lemon

1 kg (2 lb 4 oz) mixed summer
   berries, including blueberries,
   loganberries, raspberries and
   strawberries

extra fresh berries, to serve

Raspberry cream

250 g (9 oz/2 cups) fresh raspberries

50 g (1¾ oz/½ cup) icing
   (confectioners') sugar

125 ml (4 fl oz/½ cup) extra-light
   thickened (whipping) cream

Prep time 15 minutes + 7 hours
freezing

Cooking time nil

Serves 10

1 Put 500 ml (17 fl oz/2 cups) water in a saucepan and
add the sucralose. Heat gently over low heat until the
sucralose has dissolved. Bring to the boil, then reduce
the heat and simmer for 5 minutes. Set aside to cool,
then stir in the lemon juice.

2 Put sweet syrup and mixed berries in a large processor
fitted with the metal blade and blend for 20 seconds, or
until smooth. Press purée through a sieve in batches
and pour into a wide, deep plastic container.

3 Freeze the mixture for 1–2 hours, or until ice crystals
have formed around the edges. Using an immersion
blender or blender, blend to break up the ice crystals.
Return to the freezer and repeat this process for
4–5 hours until the berry mixture resembles soft snow.
Remove from freezer 15–20 minutes before serving.

4 To make the raspberry cream, blend the raspberries and
icing sugar in a small processor for 10 seconds, or until
smooth. Press through a fine sieve. Lightly whip the
cream until it just holds its shape. Fold the cream into
the raspberry purée.

5 Serve the frozen sundae mixture in chilled glasses with
a spoonful of raspberry cream and some fresh berries.

Peach yoghurt mousse

125 g (4½ oz/1 cup) dried peaches

250 ml (9 fl oz/1 cup) peach nectar

2 tsp powdered gelatine

200 g (7 oz/¾ cup) reduced-fat plain yoghurt

2–3 tsp honey, to taste

3 egg whites

2 tbsp toasted flaked almonds, to serve

Prep time 15 minutes + 1 hour refrigeration
Cooking time 10 minutes
Serves 4

1 Put the peaches and peach nectar in a small saucepan. Cook over low heat, stirring often, for 10 minutes, or until the peaches are soft and pulpy. Set aside to cool for 10 minutes.

2 Put 2 tablespoons of hot water in a small bowl and sprinkle the gelatine over the top. Whisk with a fork for 1 minute, or until the gelatine has dissolved.

3 Put the peach mixture, gelatine mixture and yoghurt in a small processor or blender fitted with the metal blade. Process for 20–30 seconds, or until smooth. Add the honey, to taste, and blend to combine.

4 Whisk the egg whites until firm peaks form. Pour the peach mixture into the egg whites and gently fold through using a metal spoon.

5 Spoon the mousse into four 250 ml (9 fl oz/1 cup) parfait glasses smoothing the surface. Cover and refrigerate for at least 1 hour, or until firm. Serve sprinkled with the almonds.

Stewed pear, apple and rhubarb

2 tbsp blackcurrant syrup

2 large pears, peeled, cored and quartered

1 apple, peeled, cored and quartered

500 g (1 lb 2 oz) rhubarb, trimmed, cut into 3 cm (1¼ in) pieces

500 ml (17 fl oz/2 cups) skim milk

55 g (2 oz/¼ cup) caster (superfine) sugar

1½ tbsp custard powder

Prep time 20 minutes

Cooking time 20 minutes

Serves 4

1 Put the syrup, pears, apple and 60 ml (2 fl oz/¼ cup) water in a large saucepan and stir to coat the fruits. Cook, covered, over low heat for 4 minutes, then add the rhubarb. Toss well to combine, then cover and cook for a further 6–7 minutes, or until the fruit is just tender. Remove from the heat, cover and leave to stand.

2 Put milk and sugar in a saucepan. Bring to the boil, then reduce heat and simmer for 3 minutes. Mix custard powder with 1 tablespoon water to a smooth paste. Return milk to the boil, stir in custard powder mixture and whisk constantly until the mixture boils and thickens, and can coat the back of a wooden spoon.

3 Put fruit in serving dishes and drizzle with any liquid from the bottom of the pan. Serve with warm custard.

Sticky fig and hazelnut puddings

45 g (1½ oz/⅓ cup) hazelnuts

150 ml (5 fl oz) fresh orange juice

100 g (3½ oz/½ cup) chopped dried figs, plus 6 dried figs, extra, cut horizontally

¼ tsp ground ginger

¼ tsp ground cinnamon

3 tsp finely grated orange zest

½ tsp bicarbonate of soda (baking soda)

60 g (2¾ oz) canola margarine, softened

115 g (4 oz/½ cup) soft brown sugar

1 egg

90 g (3¼ oz/¾ cup) self-raising flour

2 tbsp maple syrup

boiling water, for steaming

low-fat vanilla custard or cream, to serve

Prep time 25 minutes
+ 10 minutes cooling time
Cooking time 45 minutes
Serves 6

1 Preheat the oven to 200°C (400°F/Gas 6). Spread the hazelnuts out on a tray and place in the oven for 6–7 minutes, until lightly toasted. Tip the nuts onto a clean tea towel (dish towel) and gently rub to remove skins. Put the nuts in a food processor and pulse until finely ground. Grease six 250 ml (9 fl oz/1 cup) ramekins or ovenproof teacups and place a square of baking paper in the base of each.

2 Pour the orange juice into a saucepan and bring to the boil over medium heat. Add the chopped figs, ginger, cinnamon and 1 teaspoon of the orange zest and cook for 1 minute. Remove from the heat and add the bicarbonate of soda (allowing the mixture to froth), then set aside to cool for 10 minutes.

3 Meanwhile, combine margarine and sugar in a large bowl and beat until light and fluffy. Add egg and beat well. Fold in hazelnuts, and add flour in three batches, incorporating each batch well before adding the next. Pour orange sauce into pudding mixture and stir well.

4 Pour maple syrup into base of ramekins and top with remaining orange zest. Arrange two extra fig halves in the base of each ramekin. Spoon in pudding mixture until each ramekin is three-quarters full, then cover securely with a square sheet of foil. Arrange puddings in base of a deep roasting tin. Fill baking tin with enough boiling water to come halfway up sides of ramekins, and bake puddings for 35 minutes, or until cooked. Set ramekins aside for 5 minutes before inverting onto a plate and serving with custard or cream.

Couscous and apricot puddings

90 g (3¼ oz/½ cup) dried apricots, chopped

875 ml (30 fl oz/3½ cups) apricot nectar

1 tbsp grated lemon zest

1 vanilla bean, split, seeds scraped

1 cinnamon stick

1/4 tsp ground cloves

1 tbsp lemon juice

185 g (6½ oz/1 cup) couscous

low-fat vanilla custard, to serve

Prep time 20 minutes

Cooking time 45 minutes

Serves 6

1 Grease six 250 ml (9 fl oz/1 cup) pudding bowls or ovenproof teacups and put a round of baking paper in the bottom of each. Combine the apricots, nectar, lemon zest, vanilla bean and seeds, and cinnamon stick in a saucepan over medium heat and bring to the boil.

2 Reduce the heat and simmer for 5 minutes, then remove from the heat and leave for 5 minutes. Strain, reserving the apricots and discarding the vanilla bean and cinnamon stick. Return the nectar to the saucepan and divide the apricots among the pudding bowls.

3 Add the cloves, lemon juice and couscous to the reserved apricot nectar. Bring to the boil, then reduce the heat to low and simmer, covered, for 8–10 minutes, or until most of the liquid has been absorbed. The mixture should still be quite wet.

4 Spoon the couscous into the pudding bowls, level the top and cover each with a round of foil. Place the bowls in a steamer and cover with a lid. Sit the steamer over a saucepan or wok of boiling water and steam for 30 minutes, checking the water level regularly.

5 To serve, turn the puddings out of the bowls and serve hot with custard.

Pear and ginger filo parcels

**30 g (1 oz/¼ cup) flame raisins or
other small seedless raisins**

1 tbsp cognac or pear eau-de-vie

2 tsp lemon juice

3 Bosc pears

**50 g (1¾ oz) ginger nut biscuits
(ginger snaps), roughly broken**

40 g (1½ oz/¼ cup) soft brown sugar

½ tsp mixed (pumpkin pie) spice

2 tbsp cornflour (cornstarch)

1 egg yolk

8 sheets filo pastry

canola oil spray

icing (confectioners') sugar, to serve

**softened low-fat vanilla ice cream,
to serve**

Prep time 30 minutes
Cooking time 25 minutes
Serves 4

1 Preheat the oven to 190°C (375°F/Gas 5). Line a baking tray with baking paper.

2 Put raisins and liqueur in a small bowl and set aside. Put lemon juice in a bowl. Peel, quarter and core pears. Add to the bowl and toss to coat with lemon juice.

3 Put ginger nut biscuits in a blender and add sugar, mixed spice and cornflour. Blend for 15 seconds, or until mixture forms fine crumbs. Roughly chop half the pears and add to the processor. Add egg yolk and blend in 2-second bursts for 15–25 seconds, or until pears are chopped medium–fine. The mixture will be quite thin.

4 Cut the remaining pears into 2 cm (¾ in) dice and return to their bowl. Add the raisin mixture and processed pear mixture and toss to combine.

5 Lay a sheet of filo on a work surface and spray with oil. Fold in half, one short side over the other and spray with oil. Top with another sheet of filo, fold that in half and spray with oil, giving four layers of pastry. Trim the pastry to an 18 cm (7 in) square. Spoon one-quarter of pear filling onto centre. Starting at one corner, fold filo over filling to make a fat, square envelope. Ensure that the filling is well contained, and spray dry surfaces of the pastry as you fold. Spray the parcel all over with oil and place on the prepared tray, fold side up. Make three more parcels using the remaining pastry and filling.

6 Bake for 20–25 minutes, or until parcels are crisp and golden. Serve hot, dusted with icing sugar and with a little softened vanilla ice cream spooned on top.

nutrition per serve   Energy **978 kJ (234 Cal)** Fat **4 g** Saturated fat **1.3 g**
Protein **6 g** Carbohydrate **43.3 g** Fibre **2.3 g** Cholesterol **47 mg** Sodium **157 mg**

Chocolate cake with strawberries

3 eggs

185 g (6½ oz/1 cup) lightly packed
 soft brown sugar

40 g (1½ oz) reduced-fat canola oil
 margarine, melted

170 ml (5½ fl oz/⅔ cup) ready-made
 apple sauce

60 ml (2 fl oz/¼ cup) skim milk

85 g (3 oz/⅔ cup) unsweetened
 cocoa powder

185 g (6½ oz/1½ cups) self-raising
 flour

strawberries, to serve

chocolate icing

125 g (4½ oz/1 cup) icing
 (confectioners') sugar, sifted

2 tbsp unsweetened cocoa powder

1–2 tbsp skim milk

Prep time 20 minutes
Cooking time 40 minutes
Serves 12

1 Preheat the oven to 180°C (350°F/Gas 4). Brush a 20 cm (8 in) kugelhopf tin with melted butter, dust lightly with flour and shake out any excess.

2 Whisk eggs and sugar in a bowl for 5 minutes, or until pale and thick. Combine the margarine, apple sauce and milk in a small bowl, stirring to mix well, then fold into the egg mixture. Sift the cocoa powder and flour together into a bowl, then fold into the egg mixture.

3 Pour mixture into tin and bake for 35–40 minutes, or until a skewer inserted into the centre of the cake comes out clean. Leave the cake to cool in the tin for 5 minutes, then turn out onto a wire rack to cool completely.

3 To make the chocolate icing, combine the icing sugar and cocoa powder in a bowl, then stir in enough milk to form a thick paste. Stand the bowl over a saucepan of simmering water, stirring until the icing is smooth, then remove from the heat. Spread the icing over the cake and and arrange a few unhulled strawberries over the top. Hull and chop remainder of the strawberries and serve with the cake.

nutrition per serve Energy **1048 kJ (250 Cal)** Fat **4.8 g** Saturated fat **1.5 g**
Protein **4.7 g** Carbohydrate **46.1 g** Fibre **3.9 g** Cholesterol **5 mg** Sodium **91 mg**

Nectarine crumble

3 tbsp maple syrup

1 tsp finely grated lime zest

4 ripe nectarines, cut in half, stones removed

30 g (1 oz/¼ cup) self-raising flour

30 g (1 oz) light canola margarine

2 tbsp soft brown sugar

low-fat vanilla ice cream, to serve

1 Put the maple syrup and lime zest in a bowl. Stir well and leave to infuse for 15 minutes.

2 Heat the grill (broiler) to medium. Lightly brush the cut side of the nectarine halves with some of the syrup. Put the nectarine halves, cut side down, in a lightly oiled non-stick frying pan. Gently fry over low–medium heat for 1 minute on each side, or until slightly soft.

3 Put flour in a small bowl and add butter. Using your fingertips, rub the butter into flour until the mixture resembles breadcrumbs, then stir through sugar.

4 Sit the nectarines on the grill tray, cut side up. Lightly brush them with a little more syrup, then sprinkle the crumble mixture over the top and grill for 2 minutes, or until the crumble turns golden brown. Divide among four serving bowls and drizzle with the remaining syrup. Serve with a scoop of low-fat vanilla ice cream.

Prep time 20 minutes +
15 minutes infusing time
Cooking time 5 minutes
Serves 4

nutrition per serve
Energy **916 kJ (219 Cal)** Fat **10.4 g** Saturated fat **1 g**
Protein **5.4 g** Carbohydrate **25.1 g** Fibre **2.5 g** Cholesterol **32 mg** Sodium **194 mg**

Cinnamon, apple and walnut cake

Prep time 20 minutes
Cooking time 50 minutes
Serves 10–12

canola oil spray

250 g (9 oz/1²⁄₃ cups) stoneground self-raising flour

2 tsp ground cinnamon

½ tsp baking powder

55 g (2 oz/½ cup) ground almonds

55 g (2 oz/¼ cup) caster (superfine) sugar

2 apples, peeled, cored and diced

60 g (2¼ oz/½ cup) chopped walnuts

2 eggs

125 ml (4 fl oz/½ cup) buttermilk

140 g (5 oz/½ cup) unsweetened apple purée

2 tbsp canola oil

1 Preheat the oven to 180°C (350°F/Gas 4). Spray a
23 cm (9 in) round cake tin with oil, then line the base
with baking paper.

2 Sift the flour, cinnamon and baking powder into a large
bowl, then return any husks to the bowl. Stir in the
ground almonds and sugar, then the diced apple and
chopped walnuts.

3 Whisk together eggs, buttermilk, apple purée and oil in
a bowl. Add to flour mixture, then stir until combined.
Spoon into prepared tin smoothing the surface.

4 Bake for 50 minutes, or until cooked when tested with a
skewer. Leave in tin for 15 minutes, then turn out onto
a wire rack to cool. Cut into wedges to serve.

Prune and pecan loaf

canola oil spray

60 g (2¼ oz) light canola margarine

80 g (2¾ oz/⅓ cup) raw sugar

1 tsp natural vanilla extract

250 g (9 oz/1 cup) chopped pitted prunes

60 g (2¼ oz/½ cup) pecans, chopped

250 g (9 oz/1⅔ cups) stoneground self-raising flour

1 tsp freshly grated nutmeg

60 g (2¼ oz/½ cup) unprocessed barley bran or oat bran

Prep time 15 minutes

Cooking time 45 minutes

Makes 10–12 slices

1 Preheat the oven to 170°C (325°F/Gas 3). Spray a 19.5 x 9.5 cm (7½ x 3¾ in) loaf tin with oil, then line the base with baking paper.

2 Put the margarine, sugar, vanilla, chopped prunes and pecans in a large bowl. Pour over 250 ml (9 fl oz/1 cup) boiling water and stir to just melt the margarine.

3 Sift the flour and nutmeg into the bowl, then add the barley bran and return any husks to the bowl. Stir until well incorporated. Spoon into the prepared tin smoothing the surface.

4 Bake for 45 minutes, or until cooked when tested with a metal skewer. Cover with foil if the top is browning too much. Leave in the tin 10 minutes, then turn out onto a wire rack to cool. Cut into slices to serve. Serve warm or cold. Delicious toasted.

nutrition per serve Energy **752 kJ (180 Cal)** Fat **0.9 g** Saturated fat **0.2 g**
Protein **4.2 g** Carbohydrate **37.4 g** Fibre **3.9 g** Cholesterol **1 mg** Sodium **106 mg**

Apricot and fig bran bread

canola oil spray

**110 g (3¾ oz/1 cup) unprocessed
oat bran**

**250 ml (9 fl oz/1 cup) skim or
no-fat milk**

**80 g (2¾ oz/½ cup) dried apricots,
quartered**

**110 g (3¾ oz/½ cup dried figs,
quartered**

185 g (6¼ oz/1 cup) soft brown sugar

150 g (5½ oz/1 cup) self-raising flour

1 tsp ground cinnamon

1 Preheat the oven to 180°C (350°F/Gas 4). Spray a
10 x 18 cm (4 x 7 in) loaf tin with the oil and line the
base with baking paper.

2 Put the bran in a large bowl. Stir in the milk, dried fruit
and sugar. Set aside for 10 minutes to soften the bran.

3 Meanwhile, sift the flour and cinnamon into a bowl.
Stir the combined flour and cinnamon into the bran
mixture. Pour into the prepared tin and bake for
45 minutes, or until cooked when a skewer inserted
into the centre of the loaf comes out clean. Cool in
the tin for 10 minutes, then turn out. Cut into thick
slices to serve.

Prep time 15 minutes +
10 minutes soaking time
Cooking time 45 minutes
Makes 1 loaf (10–12 slices)

nutrition per serve
Energy **834 kJ (199 Cal)** Fat **1 g** Saturated fat **0.3 g**
Protein **2.6 g** Carbohydrate **45 g** Fibre **2.9 g** Cholesterol **16 mg** Sodium **86 mg**

Fruit and tea loaf

500 g (1 lb 2 oz/2¾ cups) mixed dried fruit

185 ml (6 fl oz/¾ cup) strong, hot black tea

125 g (4½ oz/¾ cup) lightly packed soft brown sugar

1 egg, lightly beaten

125 g (4½ oz/1 cup) plain (all-purpose) flour

¾ tsp baking powder

1 tsp ground cinnamon

¼ tsp ground nutmeg

a large pinch of ground cloves

Prep time 20 minutes
+ 3 hours soaking
Cooking time 1 hour 35 minutes
Serves 10–12

1 Combine the fruit and hot tea in a large bowl, cover with plastic wrap and leave for 3 hours or overnight. Preheat the oven to 160°C (315°F/Gas 2–3). Grease a 25 x 11 cm (10 x 4¼ in) loaf tin and line the base with baking paper. Dust the sides of the tin with a little flour, shaking off any excess.

2 Stir the sugar and egg into the fruit mixture and combine well. Sift the flour, baking powder and spices into a bowl, then add the fruit mixture. Using a large slotted spoon, stir to combine well.

3 Spoon mixture into tin and bake for 1 hour 35 minutes, covering the top with foil if it browns too quickly. The loaf is cooked when a skewer inserted into the centre of the loaf comes out clean. Cool the loaf in the tin, then turn out and serve.

nutrition per serve Energy **1112 kJ (266 Cal)** Fat **5 g** Saturated fat **0.6 g**
Protein **5.7 g** Carbohydrate **47.9 g** Fibre **3.2 g** Cholesterol **16 mg** Sodium **172 mg**

Italian dried fruit buns

90 g (3¼ oz/¾ cup) raisins

3 tsp instant dried yeast

80 g (2¾ oz/⅓ cup) caster (superfine) sugar

400 g (14 oz/3 cups) strong flour

35 g (1¼ oz/¼ cup) unprocessed wheat or oat bran

1 tsp almond essence

1 tbsp olive oil

finely grated zest from 1 orange

40 g (1½ oz/¼ cup) mixed peel

40 g (1½ oz/¼ cup) pine nuts

1 egg, lightly beaten

115 g (4 oz/½ cup) caster (superfine) sugar, extra

Prep time 30 minutes
+ 20 minutes soaking
+ 2 hours 50 minutes rising time
Cooking time 15 minutes
Serves 12

1 Cover raisins with 250 ml (9 fl oz/1 cup) boiling water in a small bowl and set aside for 20 minutes. Drain, reserving liquid. Put half liquid into a bowl, add yeast, a pinch of the sugar and 30 g (1 oz/¼ cup) of the flour. Stir to combine, then leave in a draught-free place for 10 minutes, or until the yeast is foamy.

2 Add remaining flour, bran, sugar into bowl of an electric mixer with a dough hook attachment and make a well in the centre. Combine remaining raisin water with almond essence and oil, then pour it, along with yeast mixture, into well. Add raisins, orange zest, mixed peel and pine nuts. With mixer set to low, mix until a dough forms. Increase speed to medium and knead dough for 5 minutes, or until it is smooth and elastic; add a little more flour if necessary. Alternatively, mix dough by hand using a wooden spoon, then turn out onto a floured work surface and knead for 10 minutes.

3 Grease a large bowl with oil, then transfer dough to bowl, turning dough to coat in oil. Cover with plastic wrap and leave to rise in a draught-free place for 2 hours, or until dough has doubled in size. Knock back by punching it gently, then turn out onto a floured work surface. Divide dough into 12 equal portions and shape each piece into an oval. To glaze the rolls, coat them in egg, then roll them in the extra sugar to coat. Transfer to a greased baking tray and leave for 30–40 minutes, or until rolls have risen a little. Meanwhile, preheat oven to 200°C (400°F/Gas 6). Bake for 15 minutes, or until golden, transfer to a wire rack to cool.

nutrition per serve Energy **704 kJ (168 Cal)** Fat **3.4 g** Saturated fat **1.1 g**
Protein **4.5 g** Carbohydrate **29 g** Fibre **3.2 g** Cholesterol **16 mg** Sodium **188 mg**

Apple and peach muffins

canola oil spray

150 g (5½ oz/1 cup) plain
   stoneground self-raising flour

80 g (2¾ oz/½ cup) wholemeal
   stoneground self-raising flour

1½ tsp ground cinnamon

½ tsp baking powder

50 g (1¾ oz/½ cup) rolled barley
   or oats

60 g (2¼ oz/⅓ cup) soft brown sugar

150 g (5½ oz/1 cup) dried peaches,
   chopped

1 large green apple, peeled, cored
   and finely chopped

1 egg

250 ml (9 fl oz/1 cup) skim milk

60 g (2¼ oz) reduced-fat canola
   margarine, just melted

1 Preheat the oven to 170°C (325°F/Gas 3). Spray twelve
80 ml (2½ fl oz/⅓ cup) muffin holes with oil.

2 Sift the flours, cinnamon and baking powder into a
large bowl, then return any husks to the bowl. Stir in
the rolled barley, brown sugar, chopped peaches and
chopped apple. Make a well in the centre.

3 Whisk together the egg, milk and melted margarine
and stir into the flour mixture until just combined.
Do not overmix. Spoon evenly into the muffin holes.

4 Bake for 20–25 minutes, or until firm to touch and
golden brown. Leave in tin for 5 minutes, then turn out
onto a wire rack to cool. Delicious served warm or cold.

Prep time 20 minutes

Cooking time 25 minutes

Makes 12

nutrition per serve Energy **805 kJ (192 Cal)** Fat **3.3 g** Saturated fat **0.5 g**
Protein **6.3 g** Carbohydrate **32.2 g** Fibre **5.1 g** Cholesterol **16 mg** Sodium **204 mg**

Fruit muffins

160 g (5¾ oz/1 cup) chopped mixed dried fruit
(apricots, dates, peaches or fruit medley with peel)

225 g (8 oz/1½ cups) wholemeal self-raising flour

1 tsp baking powder

150 g (5½ oz/1 cup) unprocessed oat bran

60 g (2¼ oz/⅓ cup) brown sugar

300 ml (10½ fl oz) skim milk

1 egg

1 tbsp oil

1 Preheat the oven to moderate 180°C (350°F/Gas 4).
Grease twelve ½ cup (125 ml) muffin holes. Soak the
dried fruit with 60 ml (2 fl oz/¼ cup) boiling water for
5 minutes.

2 Sift the flour and baking powder into a large bowl,
returning the husks to the bowl. Stir in the oat bran and
sugar and make a well in the centre.

Prep time 15 minutes + 5 minutes
soaking
Cooking time 20 minutes
Serves 12

3 Combine the milk, egg and oil in a jug. Add the soaked
fruit and milk mixture all at once to the dry ingredients.
Fold in gently using a metal spoon, until just
combined—do not overmix.

4 Divide the mixture evenly among the muffin holes. Bake
for 20 minutes, or until the muffins are risen and
golden, and a skewer inserted into the centre comes out
clean. Cool for a few minutes in the tin, then turn out
onto a wire rack. Serve warm or at room temperature.

Index

Index

A

age, and cholesterol 10
alcohol 11, 17–18
Alsace mushroom soup 67
angina 9
antioxidants 17, 18, 20–1
apples
    apple and peach muffins 184
    cinnamon, apple and walnut
      cake 178
stewed pear, apple and rhubarb
    171
apricots
    apricot and fig bran bread 180
    couscous and apricot puddings
      174
Asian greens with chilli marinade
    144
asparagus and lamb stir-fry 97
atherosclerosis 8–9, 20
avocado, sweet potatoes with
    salsa 62

B

bananaa
    banana bread with maple
      ricotta 36
    raspberry and banana smoothie
      42
beans
    beef in black bean sauce 98
    lamb with cannellini bean purée
      109
    prawns with bean and corn
      salad 58
    tuna and bean salad 76
    Vietnamese rice paper rolls 59
    white bean and chickpea dip 48
beef
    beef in black bean sauce 98
    beef with oyster sauce 102
    meatloaf 123
    pesto beef salad 78–9
    steak sandwich with onion
      relish 115
    stuffed beef fillet 122
beetroot hummus 52
beetroot, red capsicum soup 69

berries
    berry sauce 38
    chocolate cake with
      strawberries 176
    mixed berry couscous 28
    mixed berry sundae 168
    raspberry and banana smoothie
      42
    red fruit salad with berries 33
beta glucan 23
betacarotene 23
bircher muesli 31
blood clots 10, 22
blood pressure, high 11, 17, 18
blood vessels
    and cholesterol 8–9, 10
    and omega-3 oils 22
blue-eye cod in chermoula 88
body mass index (BMI) 12
broccoli with barbecued pork 94

C

cakes
    chocolate cake with
      strawberries 176
    cinnamon, apple and walnut
      cake 178
cancer 10, 22
capsicums
    beetroot and red capsicum
      soup 69
    creamy ratatouille with farfalle
      147
    pesto beef salad 78–9
caramelised onions with lentils
    155
carbohydrates 11, 19
cardiovascular disease (CVD) 7,
    9, 24
    in women 12
carrot cocktail 43
cereals 19
cerebrovascular disease 9, 10
    risk factors 11–12
chermoula 88
chicken
    chicken cacciatore 90
    chicken and mango salad 77
    chicken and sweet potato salad
      82
    chicken, vegetable lasagne 106

    lemongrass chicken 95
    Middle-Eastern chicken 103
    spicy chicken schnitzels 120–1
chickpeas
    beetroot hummus 52
    chickpea burgers 158–9
    chickpea curry 135
    chickpea fritters 61
    chickpea and vegetable salad
      73
    couscous salad 72, 121
    meatloaf 123
    prawns with bean and corn
      salad 58
    tabouleh with soy grits 54
    white bean and chickpea dip 48
    wild rice with pumpkin 134
chilli
    Asian greens with chilli
      marinade 144
    chilli tofu stir-fry 143
chocolate cake with strawberries
    176
cholesterol 8
    in food 13, 14
    good/bad 8
    HDL 8
    high 7, 10
    LDL 8–9, 10
    lowering 7
    risk factors 10
    target level 9, 14
cholesterol-reducing diet 7, 13–19
cinnamon, apple, walnut cake 178
coral trout with gremolata 91
corn
    corn cakes, tomato salsa 39
    prawns with bean and corn
      salad 58
    sweet potatoes with salsa 62
coronary heart disease 9, 10
couscous
    couscous, apricot puddings 174
    couscous salad 72
    harissa with couscous 136–7
    mixed berry couscous 28
creamy ratatouille with farfalle
    147
curry
    chickpea curry 135
    curried eggplant stir-fry 138
    jungle pork curry 92–3

D

depression 10

desserts
  chocolate cake with strawberries 176
  couscous, apricot puddings 174
  mango passionfruit sorbet 166
  mixed berry sundae 168
  nectarine crumble 177
  peach yoghurt mousse 170
  pear and ginger filo parcels 175
  pear sorbet 167
  stewed pear, apple and rhubarb 171
  sticky fig and hazelnut puddings 173
  see also cakes

diabetes 10, 11, 13, 22

diet 7, 10, 12

dips
  beetroot hummus 52
  smoky eggplant tapenade 55
  sweet potato and red lentil dip 50
  white bean and chickpea dip 48

E

eggplant
  creamy ratatouille with farfalle 147
  curried eggplant stir-fry 138
  reduced-fat moussaka 118
  smoky eggplant tapenade 55

eggs 14
  mushrooms with scrambled eggs 41
  vegetable frittata 163

exercise 10, 11, 18, 23–4

F

fast food 12

fats 14, 16, 18

fennel and orange salad 111

fettucine with seared tuna 108

fibre, soluble 19, 20, 21–2, 23

fish 22
  blue-eye cod in chermoula 88
  coral trout with gremolata 91
  fettucine with seared tuna 108
  fish tikka 86–7

giant salmon balls 114
  grilled salmon with fennel salad 111
  herbed pasta and salmon salad 75
  Italian fish rolls and sweet potato 107
  poached salmon kedgeree 124
  tuna and bean salad 76

free radicals 20

fruit 18, 20–1
  fruit frappé 40
  fruit muffins 185
  fruit and tea loaf 182
  Italian dried fruit buns 183
  poached fruit with whole spices 35
  red fruit salad with berries 33
  summer fruit soy smoothie 45

G

gender, and cholesterol 10, 12

giant salmon balls 114

ginger and pear filo parcels 175

glycaemic index (GI) 11

gremolata 91

H

harissa with couscous 136–7

HDL cholesterol 8

heart attack 7, 9, 11, 24

heredity 10

high-density lipoprotein (HDL cholesterol) 8

hydrogenation 14

hypercholesterolaemia 14

hypertension 11, 17, 18

I

inflammation 9

Italian dried fruit buns 183

Italian fish rolls and sweet potato 107

J

Jerusalem artichoke soup 64

jungle pork curry 92–3

K

kidney disease 13

kilojoule control 18

L

lamb
  lamb and asparagus stir-fry 97
  lamb with cannellini bean purée 109
  reduced-fat moussaka 118
  Scotch broth 68
  shepherd's pie 127
  tandoori lamb salad 81

lasagne
  chicken and vegetable lasagne 106
  red lentil and ricotta lasagne 150

LDL cholesterol 8
  build-up 8–9, 10

legumes 21

lemongrass chicken 95

lemongrass dressing 80

lentils
  caramelised onions, lentils 155
  red lentil, ricotta lasagne 150
  spiced pumpkin, lentil soup 70
  sweet potato and red lentil dip 50

lettuce, san choy bau 57

life expectancy 24

lifestyle 7, 23–4

lipoproteins 8

liver, functions 8

low-density lipoprotein see LDL cholesterol

M

mango
  chicken and mango salad 77
  mango passionfruit sorbet 166
  mango salsa 100, 101

margarine 17

meat
  meatloaf 123
  shish kebabs with risoni salad 112
  see also beef; chicken; lamb; pork; veal

menopause 12

Middle Eastern chicken 103
Middle Eastern potato casserole 133
minerals 20, 21
monounsaturated fats 16
    sources 16
Moroccan vegetable tagine 140–1
moussaka, reduced-fat 118
muesli
    bircher muesli 31
    muesli boost 30
muffins
    apple and peach 184
    fruit muffins 185
mushrooms
    Alsace mushroom soup 67
    mushrooms with scrambled
        eggs 41
    pâté with tortilla crisps 49

N

nectarine crumble 177
nuts 20, 21
    cinnamon, apple and walnut
        cake 178
    prune and pecan loaf 179
    sticky fig and hazelnut
        puddings 173

O

oats 23
    bircher muesli 31
    giant salmon balls 114
    muesli boost 30
    oaty buckwheat pancakes 38
    porridge with stewed rhubarb
        34
obesity 10, 11
oils 16
olives
    pasta siracusa 148
    smoky eggplant tapenade 55
    sweet potato strudel 160
omega-3 fats 13, 16, 22
omega-6 fats 16
onions
    caramelised onions, lentils 155
    red onion relish 115
oxidation 9, 20

P

pancakes, oaty buckwheat 38
pasta
    chicken and vegetable lasagne
        106
    creamy ratatouille with farfalle
        147
    fettucine with seared tuna 108
    herbed pasta and salmon salad
        75
    pasta with meatballs 104
    pasta siracusa 148
    penne with bacon, ricotta 99
    red lentil, ricotta lasagne 150
    shish kebabs with risoni salad
        112
    spinach shells in tomato sauce
        149
pâté with tortilla crisps 49
peaches
    apple and peach muffins 184
    peach and rockmelon juice 44
    peach yoghurt mousse 170
    summer fruit soy smoothie 45
pears
    pear and ginger filo parcels 175
    pear sorbet 167
    stewed pear, apple and rhubarb
        171
penne with bacon and ricotta 99
peripheral vascular disease 9
pesto beef salad 78–9
phytochemicals 20
plant foods 20–1
plant sterols 17, 23
polenta and vegetable pie 130
polyunsaturated fats 16
pork
    barbecued pork and broccoli 94
    jungle pork curry 92–3
    san choy bau 57
porridge with stewed rhubarb 34
portion sizes 19
potatoes
    giant salmon balls 114
    herbed cottage cheese potato
        60
    Middle Eastern potato casserole
        133
    shepherd's pie 127
prawn kebabs with salsa 100–1
prawns with bean, corn salad 58

processed foods 17
prune and pecan loaf 179
pumpkin
    pumpkin bhaji 142
    spiced pumpkin and lentil soup
        70
    wild rice with pumpkin 134

R

raspberry and banana smoothie
    42
raspberry cream 168
red fruit salad with berries 33
red lentil and ricotta lasagne 150
red wine 17
rhubarb
    porridge with stewed rhubarb
        34
    stewed pear, apple and rhubarb
        171
rice noodle salad, Vietnamese 80
rice paper rolls, Vietnamese 59
ricotta
    banana bread with maple
        ricotta 36
    penne with bacon and ricotta
        99
    red lentil and ricotta lasagne
        150
    reduced-fat moussaka 118

S

salads
    chicken and mango salad 77
    chicken and sweet potato salad
        82
    chickpea and vegetable salad
        73
    couscous salad 72
    fennel and orange salad 111
    herbed pasta and salmon salad
        75
    pesto beef salad 78
    red fruit salad with berries 33
    tandoori lamb salad 81
    tuna and bean salad 76
    Vietnamese rice noodle salad
        80
salmon
    giant salmon balls 114

grilled salmon with fennel salad 111

herbed pasta and salmon salad 75

poached salmon kedgeree 124

salty foods 16, 17, 22

san choy bau 57

saturated fats 8, 13

avoiding 14, 15, 18–19

sources of 10, 14, 16

Scotch broth 68

seafood

blue-eye cod in chermoula 88

coral trout with gremolata 91

fettucine with seared tuna 108

fish tikka 86–7

giant salmon balls 114

grilled salmon with fennel salad 111

herbed pasta and salmon salad 75

Italian fish rolls and sweet potato 107

poached salmon kedgeree 124

prawn kebabs with salsa 100–1

prawns with bean and corn salad 58

tuna and bean salad 76

seeds 20, 21

shepherd's pie 127

shish kebabs with risoni salad 112

silverbeet parcels 162

skewers

fish tikka 86–7

prawn kebabs with salsa 100–1

shish kebabs with risoni salad 112

smoking 12, 23, 24

smoky eggplant tapenade 55

smoothies

raspberry and banana 42

summer fruit soy 45

soluble fibre 19, 20, 21–2, 23

sorbet

mango passionfruit sorbet 166

pear sorbet 167

soup

Alsace mushroom soup 67

beetroot and red capsicum soup 69

Jerusalem artichoke soup 64

Scotch broth 68

spiced pumpkin and lentil soup 70

split pea soup 65

spices 16

spinach

spinach pie 156

spinach shells in tomato sauce 149

sweet potato strudel 160

split pea soup 65

steak sandwich with onion relish 115

sterol-enriched foods 23

sticky fig and hazelnut puddings 173

stroke 7, 9, 11

summer fruit soy smoothie 45

sweet potatoes

chicken and sweet potato salad 82

Italian fish rolls and sweet potato 107

sweet potato and red lentil dip 50

sweet potato strudel 160

sweet potatoes with salsa 62

T

tabouleh with soy grits 54

tandoori lamb salad 81

tofu

chilli tofu stir-fry 143

Vietnamese rice paper rolls 59

tomatoes

chicken cacciatore 90

pumpkin bhaji 142

spinach shells in tomato sauce 149

tomato salsa 39

trans fats 8

avoiding 15

sources of 14, 16

triglycerides 11, 18, 21, 22

tuna

fettucine with seared tuna 108

tuna and bean salad 76

V

veal

pasta with meatballs 104

veal goulash 117

vegetarian

Asian greens with chilli marinade 144

baked vegetables, rosemary 154

caramelised onions, lentils 155

chickpea burgers 158–9

chickpea curry 135

chickpea, vegetable salad 73

chilli tofu stir-fry 143

creamy ratatouille, farfalle 147

curried eggplant stir-fry 138

harissa with couscous 136–7

Middle-Eastern potato casserole 133

Moroccan vegetable tagine 140–1

pasta siracusa 148

pumpkin bhaji 142

red lentil, ricotta lasagne 150

silverbeet parcels 162

spinach pie 156

spinach shells in tomato sauce 149

sweet potato strudel 160

vegetable frittata 163

vegetable and polenta pie 130

vegetable stew with dal 152–3

wild rice with pumpkin 134

Vietnamese rice noodle salad 80

Vietnamese rice paper rolls 59

vitamins 20, 21

W

weight 10, 12

and alcohol 18

benefits of control 15

white bean and chickpea dip 48

wholegrain foods 21–2

wild rice with pumpkin 134

Y

yoghurt

peach yoghurt mousse 170

spicy yoghurt dressing 159

Contact information for high cholesterol support groups

AUSTRALIA
National Heart Foundation of Australia
Level 3, 80 William St , Sydney NSW 2011
Phone: 1300 36 27 87
Email: health@heartfoundation.org.au
Internet: www.heartfoundation.org.au

Heart Research Institute
145-147 Missenden Rd, Camperdown NSW 2050
Phone: 02 8208 8900
Internet: www.hri.org.au

NEW ZEALAND
National Heart Foundation of New Zealand
9 Kalmia St, Ellerslie Auckland 1546
Phone: 09 571 9191
Email: info@heartfoundation.org.nz
Internet: www.heartfoundation.org.nz

CANADA
Heart and Stroke Foundation of Canada
222 Queen St, Suite 1402
Ottawa ON K1P 5V9
Phone: 613 569 4361
Internet: www.heartandstroke.ca

UNITED KINGDOM
The British Heart Foundation
Greater London House. 180 Hampstead Rd
London NW1 7AW
Heart HelpLine: 0300 330 3311
Internet: www.bhf.org.uk

USA
American Heart Association
7272 Greenville Ave, Dallas TX 75231
Phone: 1 800 242 8721
Internet: www.heart.org